REVISE EDEXCEL
FUNCTIONAL SKILLS LEVEL 1

Mathematics

REVISION WORKBOOK

Series Consultant: Harry Smith

Author: Navtej Marwaha

To revise all the topics covered in this book, check out:

Revise Functional Skills Level 1
Mathematics Revision Guide 9781292145693

THE REVISE SERIES
For the full range of Pearson revision titles, visit:
www.pearsonschools.co.uk/revise

Contents

Introduction

Number

Time

Measures

Shape and space

Handling data

A small bit of small print
Edexcel publishes Sample Test Materials on its website. This is the official content and this book should be used in conjunction with it. The questions in this book have been written to help you practise what you have learned in your revision. Remember: the real test questions may not look like this.

Online test preparation

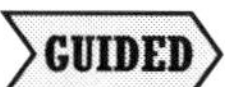

1 Match the icons with the correct statements. One has been done for you.

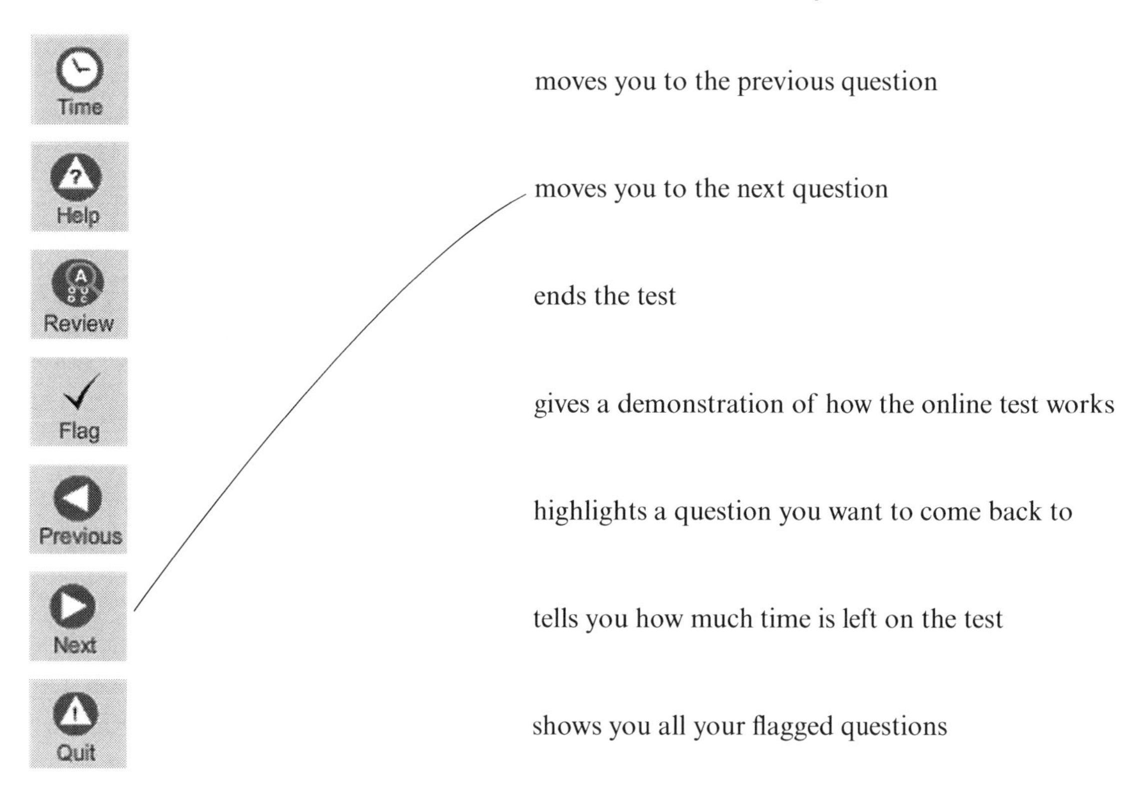

2 Look at this menu.

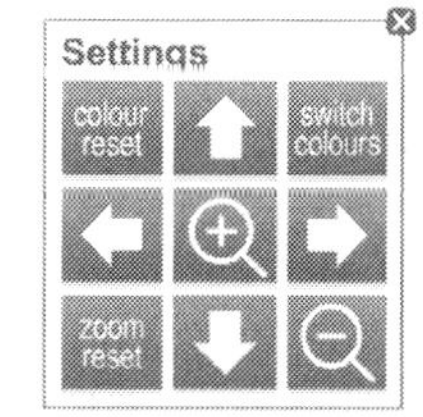

What happens when the following buttons are pressed?

(a) arrows ....

(b) magnifying glass ....

(c) colour reset ....

(d) zoom reset ....

(e) switch colours ....

3 Complete these statements.

(a) During the test you will be reminded when you have .... minutes left and again when you have .... minutes left.

(b) When you click on the help button, the .... does not stop.

(c) If the test is not clear to read, use the .... icon to change the ...., or .... in or out.

Online test tools

1 Explain the use of the following test tools during your test.

(a) ....

....

(b) ....

....

2 You are asked to organise a time plan for a day of events.

Playground | Story time | Drawing | Games | Nap

	Session 1	Session 2	Session 3	Session 4	Session 5
Group A					
Group B					
Group C					
Group D					

You decide to move 'Story time' to Session 1, Group A. How do you do this?

....

....

3 You are asked to place the home cinema on a plan so that it covers an area of 3 squares by 2 squares.

How would you do this?

home cinema

....

....

4 How do you change the position of points on a line graph?

....

....

Using the onscreen calculator

GUIDED **1** Use your calculator to work out the value of these calculations. Write down the buttons you press and the answer you get.

(a) $\frac{80 + 44 \times 4}{0.25}$ (80 + 44 × 4) ÷ 0.25 = ...

(b) $8 \times (6 - 2) + \frac{6}{2}$ ....

GUIDED **2** Crisps cost 40p per packet. A bottle of lemonade costs £1.30. Mike buys 6 packets of crisps and one bottle of lemonade. He pays with a £5 note.

Work out how much change he should get. Show the buttons that you press on the calculator to find the answer.

5 − (6 × 0.4 + 1.30) = ...

3 A machine makes 35 bolts every hour. The machine makes bolts for 8 hours each day, 5 days a week. The bolts are packed into boxes. Each box holds 25 bolts.

How many boxes are needed for all the bolts made each week? Show the buttons that you press on the calculator to find the answer.

....

....

....

4 28 children and 4 teachers went to the zoo. The cost of a ticket for a child was £7.49 and the cost of a ticket for a teacher was £13.99.

What is the total cost to get into the zoo? Show the buttons that you press on the calculator to find the answer.

....

....

....

5 Plain tiles cost £1.35 each and patterned tiles cost £4.85 each. Bernie buys 325 plain tiles and 48 patterned tiles.

Use a calculator to work out the total cost of the tiles. Show the buttons that you press on the calculator to find the answer.

> Be careful when using a calculator to carry out a long calculation. Make sure you use the correct order of operations.

....

....

....

Had a go ☐ Nearly there ☐ Nailed it! ☐

Number and place value

GUIDED **1** Write the following numbers in words.

(a) 45 672

Forty-five ....

(b) 743 508

....

GUIDED **2** Write the following numbers in figures.

(a) four hundred and six thousand, three hundred and fifty-three

406..........

(b) five million, seven hundred and thirty-four thousand, nine hundred and one

....

3 For each of these numbers, write down the value of the digit 4 in figures.

(a) 743 ....

(b) 64 799 ....

(c) 3004 ....

4 Sandeep weighs two parcels. Parcel A weighs 6435 grams and parcel B weighs 6354 grams. Which parcel is heavier?

....

....

5 The table gives information about the prices of five houses.

House	A	B	C	D	E
Price	£326,500	£278,499	£289,995	£326,550	£289,905

Write down the prices of the houses in order, starting from the least expensive.

....

....

Negative numbers

GUIDED **1** Write down the smallest and the largest number in each list.

(a) −4, −3, −8, −2, −9

smallest: .... largest: ....

(b) −12, −48, −18, −15, −53

smallest: .... largest: ....

On a number line, the numbers get **smaller** as you go to the **left**.

GUIDED **2** Write the following numbers in order from smallest to largest.

7 −13 −7 −1 −2

−13 ....

3 This table gives information about the melting and boiling points of five chemical elements.

Element	Chlorine	Hydrogen	Mercury	Nitrogen	Oxygen
Melting point (°C)	−102	−260	−39	−210	−219
Boiling point (°C)	−34	−252	356	−196	−183

Write down the name of the element that has:

(a) the lowest boiling point ....

(b) the highest melting point. ....

4 David writes down his bank balance at the end of each month for the first 6 months of the year.

Month	Jan	Feb	Mar	Apr	May	Jun
Balance (£)	−127	−48	−579	−383	−326	−398

Write down the months in order, starting with the most overdrawn and finishing with the least overdrawn.

....

....

Had a go ☐ Nearly there ☐ Nailed it! ☐

Rounding

1 Round the following numbers to the nearest ten.

(a) 43 ....

(b) 2786 ....

2 Round the following numbers to the nearest hundred.

(a) 143 ....

(b) 5869 ....

(c) 57 168 ....

3 Round the following numbers to the nearest thousand.

(a) 5869 ....

(b) 43 014 ....

(c) 623 482 ....

4 Anjali measured the weight of some objects made out of different types of materials in her engineering class. Here are her results.

Material	wood	plastic	metal
Weight (g)	21	2665	15 423

Round the weight of each material to the value stated.

(a) Weight of wood to the nearest ten grams = ...

(b) Weight of plastic to the nearest hundred grams = ...

(c) Weight of metal to the nearest thousand grams = ...

5 Alan is weighing some flour on an electronic scale. Here is the display:

237g

He records the weight as 24 grams correct to the nearest ten. Is he correct? Explain your answer.

....

....

Adding and subtracting

GUIDED **1** Simon received £325 on his birthday. He spent £179 on booking a holiday.

How much money does he have left?

£325 − £179 = £............................

2 There are 54 children on the pirate ship at a fairground. When the pirate ship stops, 38 children get off and 26 children get on. How many children are now on the pirate ship?

Subtract the number of children who get off and add the number who get on.

....

....

3 Carl buys some electrical items online. He buys a television costing £395, a DVD player costing £196, a sound bar costing £239. The electrical store charges £28 for delivery.

What is the total cost of the goods including the delivery charge?

£395 + £196 + ...

....

4 Part of this receipt is missing.

Sofa	£387
Rug	£129
Table	£

David gave the shopkeeper £750 and received £5 change.

David works out that the table must have cost £329

Look at the receipt. Is David correct? Explain your answer.

....

....

....

5 At the beginning of January, Mark had £1,840 in his bank account.

This table shows information about the amount of money he has withdrawn each month for four months.

Month	Jan	Feb	Mar	Apr
Withdrawn (£)	478	329	395	472

How much money is left in his bank account?

....

....

....

Had a go ☐ Nearly there ☐ Nailed it! ☐

Multiplying and dividing by 10, 100 and 1000

GUIDED **1** Work out the answers to these calculations.

(a) A packet contains 10 sweets. How many sweets are in nine packets?

10 × ....

(b) Each jigsaw puzzle has 1000 pieces. Tom has 7000 pieces.

How many jigsaw puzzles does Tom have?

....

2 Brian measured the length of his wardrobe door. The length of the wardrobe door was 1200 mm. He first made a scale drawing. The length of the door he drew was one hundred times smaller than the actual length of the door.

What is the length of the door he drew?

....

3 Four friends want to book a holiday for as little money as possible. They go to two high-street shops.

Top Choice

10 days @ £55 per person per night including flights and tax.

Travel Holidays

Price for two people:

10 days hotel	£1,000
Flights	£100
Tax	£10

Where should the four friends book their holiday if they want to pay as little money as possible?

....

....

4 A site manager wants to order some materials. The table shows information about the cost and quantity.

Item	Cost (£)	Quantity
bricks	120	1000
plasterboards	60	10
bolts	8	10

He orders 10 000 bricks, 10 plasterboards and 1000 bolts. What is the total cost of the order?

....

Multiplication and division

GUIDED **1** A florist sold 48 boxes of flowers. Each box contained 16 flowers.

Work out the total number of flowers sold.

total number = 48 × ....

2 Amy packs tins of fruit into boxes. Each box holds 32 tins.

How many boxes will be needed to pack:

(a) 192 tins? ....

(b) 448 tins? ....

3 A company pays some of its workers a bonus. The total amount paid out in bonuses is £11,700. This amount is split evenly between 12 workers.

How much does each worker receive?

....

....

4 343 students are going on a trip. At least one teacher must go with every 21 students.

Work out the smallest number of teachers that must go.

Remember you need a whole number of teachers. Round up your answer to the next whole number.

....

....

5 The cost price of a pram is £45. The shop sells these prams for £62. This table gives information about the number of prams sold each day in one week.

Day	Mon	Tue	Wed	Thu	Fri
Number sold	4	7	3	9	8

Work out the total profit for this week.

....

....

....

Had a go ☐ Nearly there ☐ Nailed it! ☐

Squares and multiples

GUIDED **1** Write down all the square numbers up to 100

$1^2 = 1$ $2^2 = 4$ $3^2 =$ ....

....

GUIDED **2** Write down the first ten multiples of:

(a) 8 8 16 ....

(b) 17 ....

(c) 28 ....

3 Choose one number from the box that fits each description.

21	20	25
11	8	6
10	15	32

(a) a multiple of 4 and a multiple of 5

....

(b) a square number and an odd number.

....

GUIDED **4** Find the lowest common multiples of:

(a) 6 and 9 6, 12, 18, 24... 9, 18, 27... LCM = ...

(b) 12 and 15 ....

(c) 28 and 42 ....

5 Jemima wants to make hot dogs. Hot dog sausages are sold in packs of 15 and hot dog buns are sold in packs of 8.

Work out the smallest number of packs of sausages and buns she can buy to make complete hot dogs without any buns or sausages left over.

Write down the multiples of 15 and 8, and then find the LCM.

....

....

....

Estimating

GUIDED **1** Work out an estimate for the value of:

Round both values.

(a) $93 + 48 \approx 90 + 50 =$ ....

(b) $937 - 82 \approx$ ....

(c) $178 \times 58 \approx$ ....

(d) $37.9 \div 4.95 \approx$ ....

2 Estimate each person's annual salary.

How many weeks are there in a year?

(a) David earns £288 per week. His annual salary is about ....

(b) Ethan earns £1628 per month. His annual salary is about ....

3 A farmer bought 3179 kg of fertiliser at a cost of £17 per kilogram.

Estimate the total cost of the fertiliser.

....

4 A litre of detergent will clean a patio area of about $14\,m^2$.

Estimate how many 1 litre cans are needed to clean a patio area of $123\,m^2$.

....

5 Pam sold 378 radiators for £58 each. She paid £32 each for them.

Estimate how much profit she made.

....

6 One type of coin weighs 12 g.

(a) Estimate the weight of a bag containing 167 of these coins.

....

(b) Estimate the number of these coins in a bag that weighs 983 g.

....

7 A machine operator makes 74 bolts every hour. He works 39 hours each week for 48 weeks of the year.

Estimate the number of bolts he makes in one year.

....

....

Checking your answer

GUIDED **1** Use estimation to check whether the following statements are likely to be correct.

> If the number is between 10 and 99, round to the nearest 10
>
> If the number is between 100 and 999, round to the nearest 100

(a) 68 + 93 = 161 70 + 90 = 160 so 161 is likely to be correct.

(b) 438 − 59 = 379 400 − ....

(c) 672 + 543 − 283 = 932 ....

2 Use inverse operations to check if the following statements are correct.

(a) 600 − 319 = 281 281 + 319 = ...

(b) 550 + 254 = 804 ....

(c) 963 ÷ 3 = 312 ....

(d) 211 × 12 = 252 ....

3 Alice worked out that the answer to 81 × 29 ÷ 41 is 57 to the nearest whole number.
Use estimation to decide whether she is likely to be correct.

....

....

4 Part of Leon's bank statement is shown below.

	Debit	Credit
balance brought forward		£841
restaurant	£78	
football tickets	£167	

Leon has lost the page which shows his current balance. He wants to pay for a holiday that costs £428.

Use estimation to decide whether he has enough money in his account to pay for the holiday.

....

....

....

Word problems

GUIDED **1** Rowan is going to buy a second-hand motorbike. The salesperson says Rowan can pay in cash or use a finance deal.

cash price	**finance deal**
£14,250	deposit of £2,500 + 36 monthly payments of £350

Is it cheaper to buy the motorbike with cash or with the finance deal?

2500 + (36 × ....

....

2 Eve and four of her friends want to raise £750 for charity. This table shows how much Eve's friends have raised.

Name	Shahab	Pavan	Govind	Drew
Amount raised	£192	£180	£67	£154

(a) How much money does Eve need to raise so that they have reached their target?

....

....

(b) Eve is going to swim lengths to raise the rest of the money. She will receive £6 for each length. She works out that she has to swim 26 lengths to bring the total above £750.

Is Eve correct? You must show your working.

....

....

4 Frank is planning a trip to a safari park for 6 adults and 12 children.
Here are the admission charges:

Safari park admission charges		
Adult	£26	Buy two tickets and get one free
Child	£17	Buy three tickets and get one free

The budget for the trip is £260. Is this enough money?

....

....

Had a go ☐ Nearly there ☐ Nailed it! ☐

Fractions

GUIDED **1** Write down what fraction is shaded and what fraction is not shaded.

(a)

shaded = $\frac{3}{\square}$

unshaded = $\frac{\square}{16}$

The denominator should be the total number of shapes.

(b)

shaded = ...

unshaded = ...

2 James has a bag of shapes.

What fraction of the shapes are:

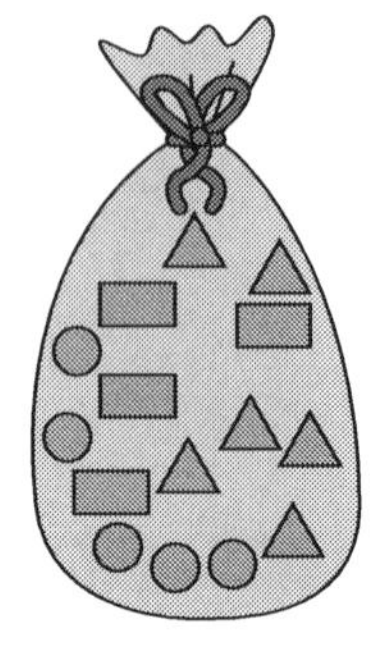

(a) triangles? ....

(b) rectangles? ....

(c) circles? ....

3 Simran is making a cake. She needs $\frac{1}{3}$ of a kilogram of sugar. She can buy packets of sugar in the following sizes: $\frac{1}{2}$kg, $\frac{1}{5}$kg and $\frac{1}{4}$kg.

What size of packet should she buy to ensure that she has enough sugar?

....

....

....

4 A box contains chocolates. There are $\frac{27}{80}$ square dark chocolates and $\frac{17}{80}$ round milk chocolates. There are 40 dark chocolates and 40 milk chocolates.

Complete the table.

	Square	Round	Total
Dark			
Milk			
Total			

Equivalent fractions

GUIDED **1** **(a)** What fraction of this shape is shaded?

Write your answer as two equivalent fractions.

$\frac{\square}{24}$ or $\frac{3}{\square}$

(b) Shade $\frac{2}{3}$ of this shape.

2 On the grids below, shade $\frac{3}{4}$ and $\frac{4}{5}$. Which is the smaller fraction?

The smaller fraction is ....

3 Which fraction is larger, $\frac{3}{5}$ or $\frac{2}{3}$?

First find the lowest common denominator.

....

....

....

4 Anna had a pizza that was cut into 8 equal slices. She ate 3 of them. Bill had a pizza that was the same size, but his was cut into 4 equal slices. He also ate 3 slices.

Who ate more pizza, Anna or Bill?

....

....

....

5 During a practice session, a trainer asks athletes to jog a certain number of laps.
Sarah jogged $\frac{3}{4}$ of the laps. Jason jogged $\frac{3}{5}$ of the laps. Tim jogged $\frac{1}{2}$ of the laps.

Order the fractions from smallest to largest.

....

....

....

Had a go ☐ Nearly there ☐ Nailed it! ☐

Mixed numbers

GUIDED **1** Change each mixed number into an improper fraction.

(a) $3\frac{1}{5}$ $\frac{5 \times 3 + 1}{5} = \frac{\square}{5}$

(b) $2\frac{1}{3}$ ....

(c) $5\frac{1}{7}$ ....

GUIDED **2** Change each improper fraction into a mixed number.

(a) $\frac{11}{2}$ $11 \div 2 = 5$ remainder 1 so $\frac{11}{2} = 5\frac{\square}{2}$

(b) $\frac{11}{5}$ ....

(c) $\frac{41}{4}$ ....

GUIDED **3** Draw lines to match the equivalent fractions. One has been done for you.

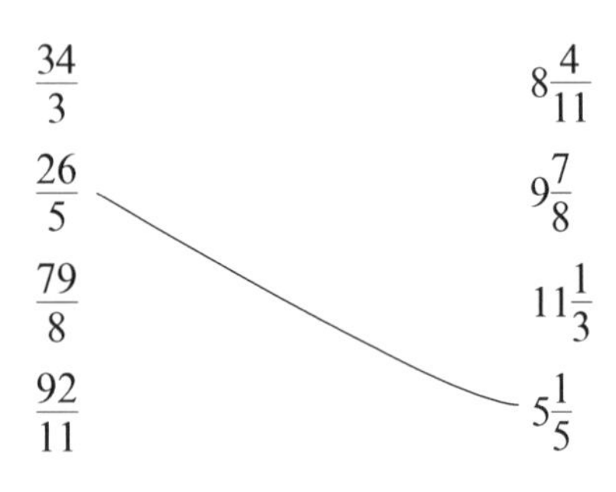

4 For each pair of fractions, write down which is smaller.

(a) $\frac{10}{3}$ or $3\frac{1}{4}$ ....

(b) $\frac{6}{5}$ or $1\frac{2}{5}$? ....

5 Tania thinks that $\frac{11}{9}$ is the same as $1\frac{1}{8}$.

Is she correct? Explain your reasoning.

....

....

....

Fractions of amounts

GUIDED **1** Find these fractions of amounts.

$\frac{3}{4}$ of 60 means $\frac{3}{4} \times 60$

(a) $\frac{3}{4}$ of 60 $\frac{3}{4} \times 60 = \frac{3 \times 60}{4} =$ ....

(b) $\frac{3}{8}$ of 160 ....

(c) $\frac{2}{3}$ of £96 ....

GUIDED **2** A factory employs 195 people and $\frac{3}{5}$ are men.

(a) How many men does the factory employ?

....

(b) How many women does the factory employ?

$\frac{2}{5} \times 195 =$ ....

3 An online company delivers 250 000 parcels a year. $\frac{1}{5}$ are delivered to Europe, $\frac{2}{5}$ are delivered to Asia and $\frac{1}{10}$ are delivered to the USA.

How many parcels are delivered to:

(a) Europe? ....

(b) Asia? ....

(c) the USA? ....

4 Amy earns £2,100 each month and saves $\frac{2}{5}$ of this. Brian earns £1,800 and saves $\frac{4}{9}$ of this.

Who saves more money each month?

Don't just write down a name. Show your working and then write a conclusion.

....

....

....

5 Julie buys 120 flowers for £40. She sells one quarter of the flowers for £2 each, one third of the flowers for £3 each and the remaining flowers for £1 each.

Work out Julie's total profit.

....

....

....

Had a go ☐ Nearly there ☐ Nailed it! ☐

Word problems with fractions

GUIDED **1** Yves shares a bag of 30 sweets with his friends. He gives Mandy $\frac{2}{5}$ of the sweets. He gives Sam $\frac{1}{10}$ of the sweets. He keeps the rest for himself.

How many sweets does Yves keep for himself?

Mandy gets $\frac{2}{5} \times 30 =$ .... Sam gets $\frac{1}{10} \times 30 =$ ....

Yves keeps 30 − ....

2 Lewis wants to buy a new pair of trainers. There are two shops that sell the trainers he wants.

Sport4life	Trainers Limited
$\frac{2}{5}$ off the usual price of £65	$\frac{3}{10}$ off the usual price of £60

He wants to pay as little money as possible.

From which shop should he buy the trainers? Give your reasons.

....

....

3 Robert wants to buy some concrete posts. He finds two companies on the internet.

Cheap Posts	Fence World
£12 each Buy 10 and receive $\frac{1}{6}$ off.	Buy 5 posts for £70 and receive $\frac{1}{4}$ off.

Robert needs to buy 10 concrete posts.

Which shop should he buy from?

Remember to show all your working and write a conclusion.

....

....

4 If Elaine uses her railcard to buy a ticket at the station she will get a third off the normal price. The normal price of the ticket at the station is £48. If she books a ticket online she can get one fifth off the normal price. The normal price of the ticket online is £45.

Elaine wants to pay the smallest amount of money possible. Should she use her railcard or book online?

....

....

Decimals

1 In words, write the value of the given digit in each of these numbers.

(a) 8 in 19.84 ....

(b) 9 in 0.694 ....

(c) 3 in 10.703 ....

GUIDED **2** Write the following numbers in order of size, starting with the smallest.

Start with the lowest number.

3.2 6.4 6.2 12.8 1.4

1.4 ....

3 Order the prices from smallest to largest.

£15.40 £15.04 £15.05 £15.50

GUIDED **4** A scientist measured the lengths of some insects in centimetres. Order the lengths from smallest to largest.

0.71 0.711 0.713 0.7 0.06

0.06 ....

5 A plumber weighed some copper in kilograms to take to the scrapyard. Order the weights from smallest to largest.

10.83 10.8 10.825 10.779 10.88

....

6 For each pair of numbers, decide which number is larger.

(a) 12.8 and 12.567 ....

(b) 15.927 and 15.94 ....

(c) 9.004 and 9.04 ....

Had a go ☐ Nearly there ☐ Nailed it! ☐

Decimal calculations

GUIDED **1** It rained 3.58 cm on Monday and 1.89 cm on Tuesday.

Work out the total rainfall for Monday and Tuesday.

3.58 + 1.89 = ...

2 Aliya walks 1.48 miles to school and Bev walks 0.68 miles to school.

How much further does Aliya walk than Bev?

....

....

3 A swimmer swims the first half of a 100 m race in 33.82 seconds and the second half of the race in 36.79 seconds.

How long does it take him to swim the whole race?

....

....

GUIDED **4** Gemma buys some items from a gift shop.

She buys a box of chocolates costing £4.55 and two rolls of wrapping paper costing £1.35 each.

She gives the cashier a £10 note.

How much change should she receive?

4.55 + 1.35 + 1.35 = ...

....

5 Part of Aakash's receipt is missing. He gave the waiter £5 and received 57p change.

Aakash works out that the milk cost £2.48.

Is he correct? Explain your answer.

Scone	£0.85
Mug of tea	£1.59
Glass of milk	£

....

....

....

Rounding decimals and estimating

1 Round the following decimals to the nearest whole number.

(a) 3.7 ....

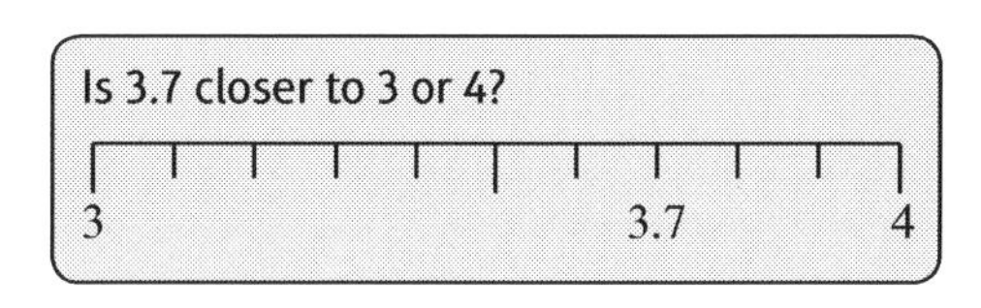

(b) 4.86 ....

(c) 11.39 ....

2 Round the following numbers to the degree stated.

(a) 4.9 m to the nearest metre. ....

(b) 10.45 cm to the nearest centimetre. ....

(c) 78.68 ml to the nearest millilitre. ....

3 Adam measures the size of his bedroom floor to decide how much carpet he needs.
He draws his results on a diagram.

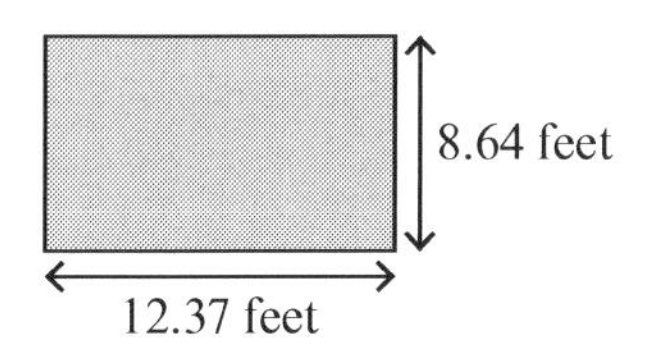

Use the ≈ sign to show the calculation is approximate.

Estimate the area of carpet that he needs.

$8.64 \approx 9$ ....

....

4 Tobias and Kaine wrote down how much money they each spent in one week.

Tobias	
sweets	£2.89
drinks	£5.21
library fine	£3.55
ice cream	90p

Kaine	
sweets	£3.97
drinks	£4.62
take away	£4.95
magazine	69p

Use estimation to decide who spent more money. You must show your working.

....

....

....

Had a go ☐ Nearly there ☐ Nailed it! ☐

Word problems with decimals

1 The cost of booking a conference room for a day is £108.50 plus £16.25 per person. A company wants to book the conference room for 3 days for 18 people.

Work out the total cost.

....

....

2 James is going to add a radiator to his study. He needs one radiator, four elbow connectors, two chrome valves and three lengths of pipe. These are the prices he finds.

1 radiator	£49.99
1 elbow connector	£1.69
1 chrome valve	£6.99
1 length of pipe	£5.79

He has a budget of £90.

Does he have enough money to add the radiator to his study?

....

....

3 Ramin is applying for jobs. He sees two jobs advertised.

Sales assistant	Sales consultant
39 hours per week	35 hours per week
£7.85 per hour	£14,500 per year

Which job pays more?

....

....

4 Alan works in a restaurant kitchen. He needs enough cream to make the desserts over the weekend. For one of the desserts he needs 25.025 litres of cream to serve all of his guests. For the other dessert he needs 33.475 litres of cream. He has already ordered 18.25 litres of cream.

How many more litres of cream should he order?

....

....

....

Fractions and decimals

GUIDED **1** Write these fractions as decimals.

(a) $\frac{3}{10}$ 3 ÷ 10 = ...

(b) $\frac{4}{25}$ ....

(c) $\frac{7}{20}$ ....

(d) $\frac{5}{8}$ ....

2 For each pair of fractions, decide which is larger.

Find the LCM for 10 and 3

(a) $\frac{3}{10}$ or $\frac{1}{3}$? ....

(b) $\frac{3}{8}$ or $\frac{4}{7}$? ....

3 For each pair of fractions, decide which is smaller.

(a) $\frac{4}{5}$ or $\frac{3}{4}$ ....

(b) $\frac{9}{16}$ or $\frac{5}{9}$ ....

4 The table shows the weights in kilograms of some pieces of timber.

Order the weights from smallest to largest.

Weight (kilograms)	$5\frac{1}{2}$	$5\frac{2}{3}$	$5\frac{7}{8}$	$5\frac{1}{4}$	$5\frac{4}{9}$
Order					

5 Jonah sells fabric on his market stall. When a customer pays a bill, it is recorded with a serial number. Jonah records the lengths of fabric with each serial number sold on in one morning.

Serial number	01045	02033	00450	01450	01549
Length (metres)	$7\frac{3}{5}$	$8\frac{1}{3}$	$7\frac{3}{8}$	$8\frac{1}{6}$	$7\frac{5}{16}$

(a) Write the serial numbers from the lowest to the highest.

....

(b) Order the lengths from shortest to longest.

....

....

Had a go ☐ Nearly there ☐ Nailed it! ☐

Percentages

1 Express each of the following as a percentage.

(a) 48 out of 100 ....

(b) $\frac{12}{100} + \frac{75}{100} + \frac{11}{100}$ ....

GUIDED **2** Alicia sells used cars. 15% of the cars in her showroom are grey, 28% are silver and 43% are black. Half of the remaining cars are red.

What percentage of the total number of cars are red?

100% − 15% − 28% − 43% = ...

3 A shop sells mobile phones. This table shows the number of mobile phones sold each month from July to December.

What percentage of the number of phones sold in total were sold in September?

Month	Jul	Aug	Sep	Oct	Nov	Dec
Number sold	12	26	4	14	11	33

....

....

....

4 Joe needs to take a gas safety qualification. He looks at two colleges where he can take the course.

College A	**College B**
89 out of 102 passed	89 out of 153 passed

Joe wants to go to the college with the greatest percentage of passes. Which college should he choose? Give a reason for your answer.

....

....

....

5 Sonia invited 100 people to a Christmas party. 48 people were adults. The rest were children. 25% of the children were 10 or older.

Work out the percentage of guests who were younger than 10.

....

....

Calculating percentage parts

GUIDED **1** Work out the answers to these calculations.

Percent means out of one hundred.

(a) 11% of 50 $\frac{11}{100} \times 50 =$ ....

(b) 7% of 225 ....

GUIDED **2** A ticket for a concert costs £98 plus a booking charge of 6%. Work out:

(a) the amount of the booking charge

For part (a), find 6% of £98. For part (b), add this amount to the original price.

$\frac{6}{100} \times$ ....

(b) the total cost of buying a concert ticket.

....

3 Candice bought a house for £67,750. After one year, the value of the house increased by 12%.
What was the value of the house after one year?

....

....

4 Kamran wants to buy a game for her new games console. She finds two online shops that sell the game she wants.

Games Online	**Gaming World**
Cost £54.40 Online discount of 15% Delivery charge of £3.25	Cost £40.80 + VAT VAT at 20% No delivery charge

Kamran wants to pay the lowest possible price. Which shop should Kamran buy her game from? You must show all your working.

....

....

....

....

Had a go ☐ Nearly there ☐ Nailed it! ☐

Fractions, decimals and percentages

GUIDED **1** Write the following amounts in order of size, starting with the smallest.

Convert all three amounts to the same form.

(a) 0.73 $\frac{7}{10}$ 71%

0.73 = 73% $\frac{7}{10}$ = 70% ....

(b) 42% 0.4 $\frac{9}{25}$

....

2 Nav earns £3,400 per month. He spends 16% of his salary as rent and $\frac{2}{5}$ of his salary on bills.

Work out how much Nav has left after he has paid his rent and bills.

....

....

3 Sabena surveyed 150 people to find out how they travel to work.

15% of the people travel to work by bus. $\frac{13}{20}$ of the people travel to work by car. The rest of the people walk to work. How many people walk to work?

....

....

4 Isaac buys 40 cases of juice for £162. He sells one quarter of the cases for £6.40 each, 35% of the cases for £5.75 each and the remaining cases for £4.25 each. Work out Isaac's total profit.

....

....

5 Harry works as a brick salesperson. He is paid £1,250 per month plus 20% commission of the total value of the bricks sold that month. In the first month, he sells bricks with a total value of £4,500.

Work out the amount of commission he was paid in the first month.

....

Word problems with percentages

1 Mark wants to buy a bike. He sees two adverts in the newspaper for the bike he wants.

Bikeys
Was £145
Now $\frac{1}{3}$ off

Cycles4u
Was £158
Now just 64% of original price

Mark has a budget of £100.Which shop can he buy the bike from?

....

2 Trevor sells two types of door. One month, he had 180 customers. 55% of them ordered wooden doors. The rest ordered double-glazed doors. The table shows the cost of each door.

Type of door	wooden	double-glazed
Cost	£89	£115

How much money did Trevor's business take that month?

....

3 Asha wants to buy a house. She has to pay an estate agent a fee to buy a house. The table gives information about an estate agent's fees for selling a house.

House price	Estate agent fee
Up to £120,000	3% of the house price
Over £120,000	3% of the first £120,000 + 2% of the remaining house price

Asha buys a house for £190,000. What fee does the estate agent charge?

....

....

4 A beach resort runs several different activities. The cost of each activity is given in this table.

Activity	paragliding	surfing	jet skiing	scuba diving
Cost	£16.75	£18.00	£23.50	£14.00

120 people took part in the activities. 25% did paragliding, 35% did surfing, and equal numbers of people did jet skiing and scuba diving. How much money did the beach resort take on that day?

....

....

Had a go ☐ Nearly there ☐ Nailed it! ☐

Using formulas

GUIDED **1** You can work out the time in minutes needed to cook a joint of beef using this rule:

weight in kg → multiply by 12 → add 20

Work out the time needed to cook a 7 kg joint of beef.

time = 7 × ....

2 Tina the plumber charges an hourly rate of £28 plus a £45 callout charge.

The amount Tina charges, in pounds, can be worked out using this formula:

cost = number of hours worked × hourly rate + callout charge

Tina works for 8 hours. Work out how much she charges.

Use the order of operations to find the correct value.

....

3 The following formula can be used to work out the cost in pounds of hiring a car.

cost = £80 + 60p per mile

Darren hires a car and drives 150 miles. Work out the cost of hiring the car for this journey.

....

4 Jerry is building a playhouse for her daughter. She uses this formula to work out how many bricks she needs:

number of bricks = area (m^2) × 60 − 80

The total area of the walls is 950 m^2. How many bricks will Jerry need?

....

Ratio

GUIDED **1** Match the equivalent ratios.

1 : 5	3 : 1
16 : 32	10 : 50
9 : 1	4 : 8
63 : 21	27 : 3

2 Write each ratio in its simplest form.

(a) 10 apples to 20 oranges 10 : 20 = 1 : ....

(b) 5 cars to 25 vans ....

(c) 45 boys to 90 girls ....

(d) 12 black tiles to 96 white tiles ....

3 Lizzy is making drinks by mixing pineapple squash with water. Here is a table of the amounts of squash that should be mixed with different amounts of water.

Amount of pineapple squash (ml)	Amount of water (ml)
5	....
1	....
8	48
....	72

(a) Complete the table.

(b) Write down the ratio of squash to water in its simplest form. ....

4 A coin is made from copper, nickel and other materials. 75% of its weight is copper and 15% of its weight is nickel. Find the ratio of the weight of copper to the weight of nickel. Give your ratio in its simplest form.

....

5 Jenny buys two bags of sweets from two different companies. They both contain a mixture of mint- and toffee-flavoured sweets.

Marivo's	**Simm's**
12 mint and 36 toffee	16 mint and 48 toffee

Are the ratios of mint-flavoured sweets to toffee-flavoured sweets in the two bags equivalent ratios? Explain your reasons.

....

....

Had a go ☐ Nearly there ☐ Nailed it! ☐

Ratio problems

1 Write the following ratios in their simplest forms.

Convert £2 to pence first.

(a) £0.25 : £2.00 ....

(b) 20 minutes : 240 minutes ....

(c) 7.5 cm : 15 mm ....

(d) 40 cm : 4 m ....

GUIDED **2** On Tuesday, Caroline spent 30 minutes travelling to see her clients and 3 hours 30 minutes working for them.

(a) Write the ratio of travel time to working time in its simplest form.

3 hours 30 minutes = 210 minutes so the ratio is ....

....

(b) On Wednesday, Caroline worked for double the time she worked on Tuesday but spent the same amount of time travelling. Write the ratio of travel time to working time on Wednesday in its simplest form.

....

....

3 Anjali and Dillon share some money in the ratio 10 : 1. Anjali receives £180. How much money do they share altogether?

....

4 An office employs managers and office staff in the ratio 3 : 9. There are 18 managers. How many office staff are there?

Simplify the ratio to make the question easier.

....

5 Ravina wants to wash her car. She needs to mix 1 part car wash to 9 parts water. Ravina uses 150 ml of car wash.

(a) How much water should Ravina use?

....

(b) On another occasion, she filled up a bucket with a total of 1800 ml of car wash and water. How much car wash and how much water did she use to make this bucket?

....

Proportion

GUIDED **1** Jen buys 3 bunches of flowers. The total cost is £23.64. Work out the cost of 11 of these bunches of flowers.

3 bunches = £23.64 so 1 bunch = £23.64 ÷ 3 = ...

....

2 A fabric shop sells material by the metre. Ravi bought 4 m of material for £26.08. What is the cost of 15 m of the same material?

....

3 Three bottles of orange juice fill 12 glasses. How many glasses can be filled from 14 bottles of orange juice?

....

4 A large carton of popcorn costs £4.55 and holds 250 g. A small carton of popcorn costs £2.85 and holds 125 g. Which carton is better value for money?

....

5 Carla is growing some vegetables in a large wooden pot. The wooden pot holds 500 ml of soil. She adds some liquid fertiliser to the soil. She needs to use 25 ml of fertiliser for every 100 ml of soil. She must add the liquid fertiliser once per month.

Show all your working and then write a conclusion.

(a) How much liquid fertiliser does Carla add to the soil each month?

....

(b) Carla thinks 1450 ml of liquid fertiliser is enough for a year. Is she correct? Show how you get your answer.

....

....

6 Jeremy wants to order some pens. He sees two offers at a stationery shop.

Offer 1	Offer 2
1 pack of pens £4.90	1 box of pens £12.20

1 pack contains 12 pens and 1 box contains 30 pens. He wants to order 120 pens.

Which offer would give Jeremy better value for money? You must show clearly how you get your answer.

....

....

Had a go ☐ **Nearly there** ☐ **Nailed it!** ☐

Recipes

1 Here is a list of ingredients required to make fudge for 4 people.

Fudge	
400 g sugar	8 g butter
320 g condensed milk	60 ml milk

Work out how much of each ingredient is needed to make fudge for 8 people.

....

....

2 Alice wants to make some scones. She sees a recipe in a book. It serves 6 people.

Scones	
300 g flour	50 g currants
3 eggs	150 ml milk

Work out how much of each ingredient is needed to make scones for 18 people.

....

....

....

....

3 Ramon wants to make some pancakes. He finds a recipe for 8 pancakes.

Pancakes
300 ml milk
120 g flour
1 egg
5 g butter

Ramon's ingredients
1100 ml milk
350 g flour
3 eggs
18 g butter

Ramon wants to make 24 pancakes. Does he have enough ingredients? You must show clearly how you get your answer.

....

....

....

....

Word problems with ratio

GUIDED

1 A car park has 168 cars parked in it. There are 42 diesel cars. The rest are petrol. Work out the ratio of diesel cars to petrol cars. Give your answer in its simplest form.

petrol cars = 180 − 42 = ...

....

2 Suki runs a playgroup. There must be 1 adult for every 9 children. One day, 58 children attend the playgroup. There are 6 adults. Are there enough adults for the 58 children? Show how you get your answer.

....

....

3 Asha and Fernando hire a speed boat for 21 days.

They share the total hire cost in the ratio 1 : 4

Asha pays £651. How much does Fernando pay?

....

4 Paul buys 2000 g of dog food in a bag. The label on the bag says:

Give your dog 10 g for each 500 g of its body weight each day.

Paul's dog weighs 3000 g. Paul thinks the 2000 g of dog food will last more than 4 weeks.

Is he correct? Explain your reasoning.

....

....

....

5 Siobhan is organising the flower arrangements at a wedding. She has worked out that for every rose, she will need 7 tulips. She will need 600 flowers in total. The table shows information about the cost of flowers.

Flower	rose	tulip
Cost of each flower	15p	12p

Work out how much the flowers will cost in total.

....

....

....

Had a go ☐ Nearly there ☐ Nailed it! ☐

Problem-solving practice

GUIDED **1** A hotel has different types of rooms. $\frac{2}{5}$ of the rooms are single, 25% of the rooms are double and the remaining rooms are deluxe. What percentage of rooms are deluxe?

Convert $\frac{2}{5}$ into a percentage.

deluxe rooms = 100% − 25% − ....

2 Here is the menu in Jean's cafe.

Menu	
cup of tea	£1.35
mug of coffee	£1.85
all-day breakfast	£3.89
dish of the day	£4.45

(a) Work out the total cost of 4 all-day breakfasts.

....

....

(b) Barry buys some cups of tea. He only has £10

Work out the greatest number of cups of tea he can buy.

....

(c) A child's meal costs $\frac{2}{5}$ of the cost of the dish of the day.

Work out the cost of a child's meal.

....

3 On 1 May, Gavin has £483 in his bank account.

On 17 May, he puts £184 into his bank account and four days later he puts a further £266 into his bank account.

This bank statement shows how much Gavin spends in May.

Bank statement	
mortgage	£234.67
council tax	£122.50
energy bill	£148.00
phone contract	£16.99
supermarket	£298.92

(a) Work out how much money there is in Gavin's bank account at the end of May.

....

....

(b) Gavin wants to buy a television that costs £850. He is going to pay for the television on his credit card. Gavin will have to pay back the £850 plus 18% interest.

How much interest will he pay in total?

....

....

Problem-solving practice

GUIDED **1** Debra is making some tea light decorations. A tea light decoration is made from a small candle and a holder. Debra buys some packs of small candles and some packs of holders.

There are 15 candles in a pack of small candles. There are 12 holders in a pack of holders. Debra buys exactly the same number of small candles and holders.

(a) Debra buys 4 packs of candles. How many packs of holders does she buy?

$4 \times 15 =$ ....

....

(b) Each pack of small candles cost £6.85 and each pack of holders cost £6.20. Debra uses all the tea lights and holders she has bought. She sells all the tea light decorations for £1.05 each.

How much profit does Debra make?

....

....

....

2 Karim trains in a gym for 2 hours a day. He starts his 2 hours of training with a warm-up and then does cardiovascular exercises. His trainer tells him the ratio of time spent warming up to time spent doing cardiovascular exercises should be 1 : 5. Karim does his warm up for 20 minutes.

(a) Does Karim warm up for the correct time? Explain your answer.

....

....

(b) With the remaining time he does different exercises. The table shows different exercises and calories lost in a 5 minute interval.

Exercise	running	rowing	cross training
Calories lost in 5 minutes	64	40	35

Karim runs for 45 minutes, rows for 25 minutes and for the remaining time he cross trains. Karim wants to use at least 900 calories by doing these exercises.

Does he use at least 900 calories? Explain your answer.

....

....

....

Had a go ☐ Nearly there ☐ Nailed it! ☐

Problem-solving practice

GUIDED **1** Ethan earns £2,100 each month. He asks his manager for an increase of £126 a month. The manager offers him a 5% increase.

Find 5% of £2,100

Is the offer from the manager more than Ethan asked for? You must show your working.

5% = 0.05 0.05 × £126 = ...

....

2 Andrea wants to grow onions in large plastic buckets. To fill the plastic buckets, she needs to buy 200 litres of soil. Andrea can buy the soil in 3 different sized bags.

25 litre bag	50 litre bag	20 litre bag
£2.49 each	2 for £4.85	£2.45
		Buy 4 get 1 free

Andrea wants to pay as little as possible for the soil. How much will Andrea have to pay?

....

....

3 Lisa needs 4000 kg of white gravel for her driveway. She can buy gravel in 1000 kg bulk bags or in 40 kg bags.

1000 kg bulk bag	40 kg bag
£112 each	£4.45 each, buy 3 get 1 free

Lisa wants to pay as little as possible for the gravel. How much does Lisa pay for the gravel?

....

....

4 Brett is looking at two different ways to pay his water bill. He can either have a water meter or not have a water meter.

Water meter	**No water meter**
cost = number of litres per year × £0.03 + £27.65	£72.25 per month

Brett uses 2400 litres every month. Brett wants to pay as little as possible for the water he uses. Should Brett have a water meter?

....

....

Units of time

GUIDED **1** How many seconds are there in:

(a) 4 minutes? $4 \times 60 =$ ....

(b) 1 hour? ....

2 How many minutes are there in:

(a) $\frac{1}{4}$ hour? ....

(b) 1 day? ....

3 How many hours are there in:

(a) 3 days? ....

(b) 1 week? ....

4 How many years are there in:

(a) 7 decades? ....

(b) 5 centuries? ....

5 Karim trains in a gym during the day. He does the following exercises.

Exercise	running	rowing	cross-training
Time spent on exercise	40 minutes	25 minutes	1 hour 15 minutes

What is the total time spent on the exercises?

....

6 Zach records two TV programmes. The first lasts 1 hour 25 minutes, and the second lasts 2 hours 40 minutes. How long does the recording take?

....

7 Arun is travelling to Calais from his house. It takes him 35 minutes to get to the coach station. He waits 20 minutes for the coach. The coach journey takes 1 hour 25 minutes to Dover. At Dover he waits 15 minutes for the ferry. The journey on the ferry takes 1 hour 45 minutes.

How long does he take to get to Calais from his house?

....

....

Had a go ☐ Nearly there ☐ Nailed it! ☐

Dates

GUIDED **1** This calendar shows the days in May 2016.
On Monday 2 May, Lesley books some appointments.

Write down the dates that each appointment will be on.

Sun	Mon	Tue	Wed	Thu	Fri	Sat
1	2	3	4	5	6	7
8	9	10	11	12	13	14
15	16	17	18	19	20	21
22	23	24	25	26	27	28
29	30	31				

(a) haircut in 5 days' time ....

(b) facial in 2 weeks' time ....

(c) manicure in 18 days' time ....

2 This calendar shows the days in September 2016.

If today is Monday 5 September, how many days is it until these appointments?

Sun	Mon	Tue	Wed	Thu	Fri	Sat
				1	2	3
4	5	6	7	8	9	10
11	12	13	14	15	16	17
18	19	20	21	22	23	24
25	26	27	28	29	30	

(a) doctor on 14 September ....

(b) bank manager on 24 September ....

(c) parents' evening on 30 September ....

3 These calendars show the days in October and November 2017.

October						
Sun	**Mon**	**Tue**	**Wed**	**Thu**	**Fri**	**Sat**
1	2	3	4	5	6	7
8	9	10	11	12	13	14
15	16	17	18	19	20	21
22	23	24	25	26	27	28
29	30	31				

November						
Sun	**Mon**	**Tue**	**Wed**	**Thu**	**Fri**	**Sat**
			1	2	3	4
5	6	7	8	9	10	11
12	13	14	15	16	17	18
19	20	21	22	23	24	25
26	27	28	29	30	31	

(a) How many days are there from Thursday 19 October to Thursday 16 November?

....

(b) Karen books an outbound flight for Friday 20 October. Her return flight is 17 days later.

Write down the date she flies back.

....

12-hour and 24-hour clocks

GUIDED **1** Convert the following times to 24-hour times:

(a) 10.30 a.m. 10:30 **(b)** 2.25 p.m. ....

(c) 4.28 p.m. .... **(d)** 5.15 a.m. ....

(e) 5 past midnight .... **(f)** 12.15 p.m. ....

GUIDED **2** Convert the following 24-hour times to 12-hour times:

(a) 08:32 8.32 a.m. **(b)** 15:16 ....

(c) 20:35 .... **(d)** 18:42 ....

(e) 11:45 .... **(f)** 16:30 ....

3 A train sets off from London Euston at 15:43 and arrives at Wolverhampton at 17:37.
How long does the journey take?

....

4 Jeff sets off on a bike ride at 11:20 and cycles for one and three-quarter hours. He then rests for 25 minutes and returns home by a different route which takes 2 hours and 35 minutes.

(a) What time does he finish his rest?

....

(b) What time does he arrive back home?

....

5 Amar is planning an interview schedule for four candidates. Interviews take place every 40 minutes. The first interview takes place at 09:45.

(a) Write down the times of the next three interviews.

....

(b) The length of each interview is 25 minutes. Write down the times when the first four interviews finish.

....

(c) The fourth candidate was 20 minutes late. What time did he start and finish his interview?

....

Had a go ☐ **Nearly there** ☐ **Nailed it!** ☐

Timetables

1 Here is part of a timetable for a bus from Wolverhampton to Stourbridge.

Wolverhampton	0547	0627	0657	0742
Penn	0600	0640	0710	0757
Wombourne	0607	0647	0717	0804
Kingswinford	0621	0701	0731	0819
Stourbridge	0633	0713	0743	0833

(a) Mary takes the 05:47 bus from Wolverhampton. What time does she arrive at Kingswinford?

....

(b) Kelly takes the 07:42 bus from Wolverhampton. How long does the journey take to Stourbridge?

Look across the Wolverhampton row for 0742 and read down the column.

....

2 This timetable is for the sleeper train from Fort William to London.

	Mon–Fri	Sat–Sun
Fort William	1950	1900
London	0747	0747

(a) How long does the journey take during the week?

....

(b) Does the journey take longer during the week or at the weekend?

....

3 Here is part of a train timetable from Birmingham to York.

Birmingham	0735	0800	0815	0830	0845	0900
York	0908	0938	0947	1003	1058	1038

(a) Write down the time of the train that takes longer than 2 hours.

....

(b) Michelle catches the 08:15 train from Birmingham. How long will it take her to get to York?

....

(c) Naresh has a meeting in York. He has to be in York before 10:00. Which is the latest train that he can catch?

....

Creating a time plan

1 Reema is a seamstress. The table shows the order in which she will do the jobs and the time she expects each type of job to take.

Reema starts the first job at 8 a.m. Complete the time plan for Reema's day, including the time she starts and finishes each job.

Job	Length of task	Time
Shortening trousers × 2	35 minutes each	8.00 a.m. – 9.10 a.m.
Shortening skirt	45 minutes	
Tea break	20 minutes	
Shortening sleeves on jacket	1 hour 15 minutes	
Lunch	1 hour	
Reline a jacket	2 hours 30 minutes	

2 Andrew works as a car salesperson. One day, he has to:

- hold car demonstrations at 10 a.m. and 3 p.m. (each lasting 50 minutes)
- attend in-house training from 11 a.m. to 1.15 p.m.
- meet Mr Smith to discuss new model (30 minutes)
- meet Mrs Ahmad to hand over new car (30 minutes)
- complete paperwork (1 hour).

Andrew wants to start work at 8 a.m. and finish work by 4 p.m. Make a time plan for Andrew to organise his day. Show the start time and finish time for each task.

3 The church hall is going to be hired for the end of year ball. Sameena books the hall from 5 p.m. to 1 a.m. Here are all of the events that need to take place:

- room preparation (2 hours 15 minutes)
- reception and drinks (1 hour and 15 minutes)
- meal (1 hour 30 minutes)
- speech (45 minutes)
- DJ and disco (3 hours)

Does Sameena have enough time at the church hall?

....

....

Had a go ☐ Nearly there ☐ Nailed it! ☐

Problem-solving practice

1 Sean is cycling into town. He leaves at 14:30. It takes 50 minutes to cycle to town. He spends 1 hour 40 minutes having lunch with his friends. He spends 35 minutes repairing a puncture on his bike. It then takes him 55 minutes to cycle back home. What time does Sean arrive back home?

50 mins + 1 hour 40 mins + 35 mins + 55 mins = ...

2 This table shows the amount of time it takes for some services to be completed by a mobile hairdresser.

Service	Time taken
haircut	45 minutes
shave	20 minutes
colour	1 hour 15 minutes
manicure	35 minutes

In one day, the hairdresser does 5 haircuts, 4 shaves, 3 colours and 2 manicures.

How long do these services take in total? Give your answer in hours and minutes.

....

3 Four teams enter a handball competition: Claremont, Hollybush, Pennhouse and Wells.

Each team will play each of the other teams once. The first game starts at 11.00 a.m. and each game takes 40 minutes. There is a break of 15 minutes after each game. One game is played at a time.

Design a timetable showing the start times, finish times and the teams playing each game.

4 A bank posts this schedule showing the days it is open in November and December. If the day is shaded, the bank is closed.

November						
Sun	Mon	Tue	Wed	Thu	Fri	Sat
		1	2	3	4	5
6	7	8	9	10	11	12
13	14	15	16	17	18	19
20	21	22	23	24	25	26
27	28	29	30			

December						
Sun	Mon	Tue	Wed	Thu	Fri	Sat
				1	2	3
4	5	6	7	8	9	10
11	12	13	14	15	16	17
18	19	20	21	22	23	24
25	26	27	28	29	30	31

(a) Anjali puts a cheque into her bank account on 9 November. It takes 4 working days to clear. What date does her cheque clear?

....

(b) Ravina orders a cheque book on 7 December. The bank states it will be delivered in 14 working days. What date should she receive the cheque book?

....

Problem-solving practice

1 Candice wanted to book a room at the Premier Hotel. She enquired about the hotel room on Tuesday 8 March. The hotel told Candice that a room is available on Thursday next week.

What date is the room available?

....

2 Here is part of an incomplete train timetable from London to Swansea.

Jasmine gets to the station in London at 10:43. She waits for the next train to Swansea.

London	1105	1205	1305
Swindon	1208		1409
Bristol	1234	1324	
Swansea	1402	1453	....

(a) How long does she have to wait? ....

(b) At what time should she arrive in Swansea? ....

(c) Karen gets the 1205 from London. How long does the journey take to Swansea?

....

(d) Lorna gets the 1305 train from London. It takes 2 hours 51 minutes. At what time does she arrive in Swansea?

....

3 A police academy is open from 05:30 until 23:45.

(a) How long is the academy open for? ....

(b) Janet needs to attend a compulsory course and 3 optional courses. The compulsory course lasts for 30 minutes and can be done at any time. Janet chooses to attend the compulsory course last.

The table shows the optional courses.

9:00	9:15	9:45	10:30	10:45	11:15	12:00	12:15
surveillance	finger printing	crime scenes	the law	advanced driving	self defence	health and safety	diversity
1 hr 45 mins	45 mins	1 hr	45 mins	1 hr 15 mins	45 mins	45 mins	30 mins

Janet chooses advanced driving as one of her courses. She needs a break of least 15 minutes between courses. The training day runs from 09:00 to 13:45. Design a timetable for Janet to show the start time and finish time for each course.

Had a go ☐ **Nearly there** ☐ **Nailed it!** ☐

Units

GUIDED **1** Show what these units measure by writing them into the correct column of the table.

centimetres grams centilitres tonnes millimetres kilometres millilitres litres kilograms

Weight	Distance	Capacity
kilograms		

GUIDED **2** Write an appropriate unit of measure for:

(a) the weight of a bag of onions kilograms

(b) the distance of Wolverhampton from Glasgow ....

(c) the height of a house ....

(d) the width of a piece of paper ....

3 Estimate:

(a) the height of an average female in the UK ....

(b) the weight of a pound coin ....

(c) The capacity of a can of cola. ....

4 Look at this scale drawing of a lorry driver and his truck.

The truck driver wants to drive the truck under a bridge.

The bridge is 2.5 metres high.

Can the driver safely drive the truck under the bridge?

Assume that the man is an average height and use this to estimate the height of the truck.

....

Measuring lines

1 Measure the lengths of the following lines in centimetres.

Remember to include the units.

(a) ____________________ ....

(b) __________________ ....

(c) _________ ....

2 In the space below, draw straight lines with the following lengths.

(a) 54 mm

(b) 5 cm

(c) 4.8 cm

3 Mark the midpoint of the line AB with a cross.

Measure the line and then divide by 2

A ____ B

4 Measure the perimeter of this rectangle. Give your answer in centimetres.

....

....

Scales

1 Write down each number marked with an arrow.

Work out what each increment is worth.

(a) 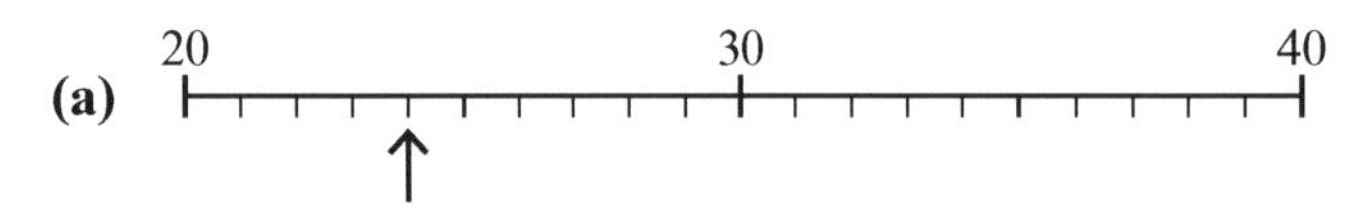

(b) 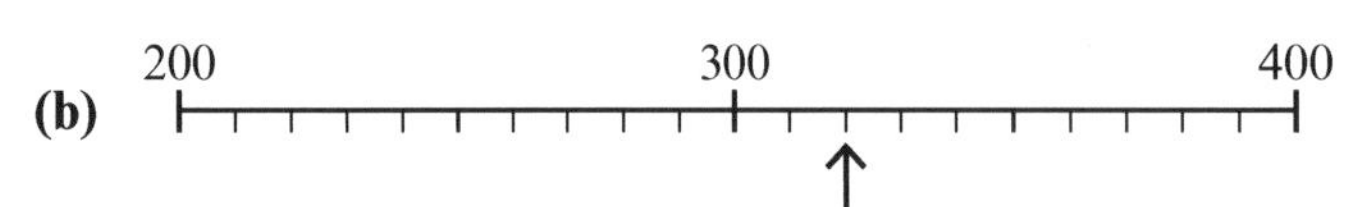

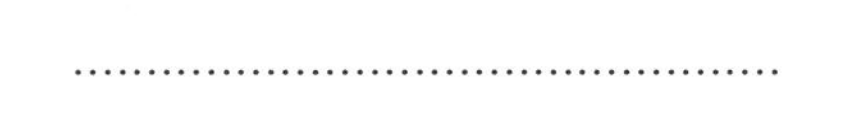

(c) 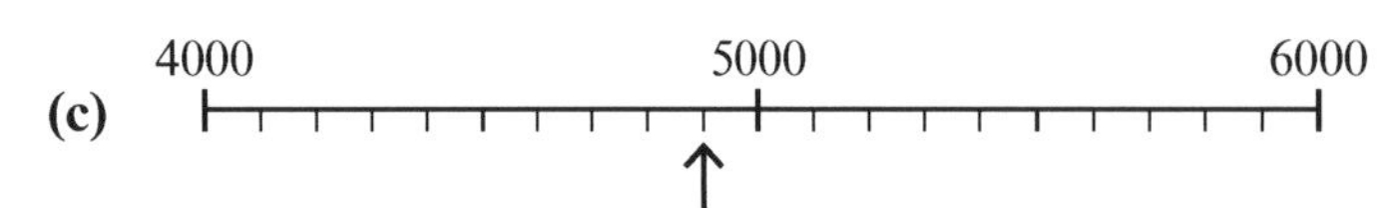

(d) 

....

2 Mark each number on the number line with an arrow.

(a) 280

(b) 3.7

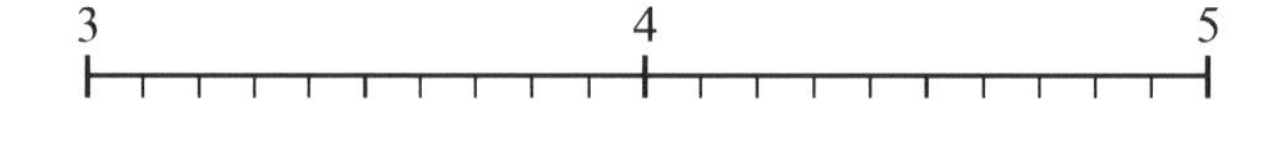

3 How much water is in this beaker?

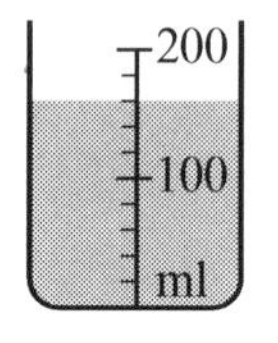

4 This diagram shows the speedometer of a car.

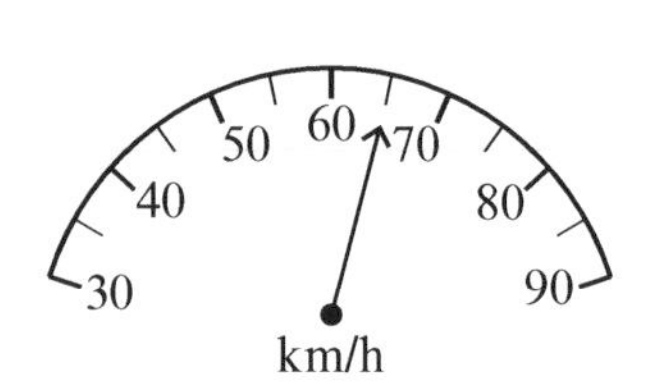

(a) Write down the speed of the car.

....

(b) Draw an arrow on the speedometer to show 55 km/h.

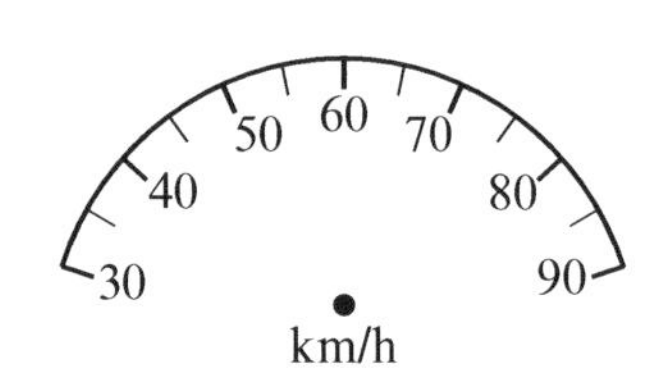

Mileage charts

1 This chart shows the distances in miles between 5 cities.

Aberdeen				
513	Bristol			
473	171	Cambridge		
595	206	124	Dover	
587	83	250	244	Exeter

Remember to include the units in your answer.

(a) Write down the distance between Bristol and Dover. ....

(b) From the table, write down the name of the city which is:

(i) nearest to Aberdeen ....

(ii) 250 miles from Cambridge. ....

2 This chart gives distances in miles by road between some towns.

Shrewsbury				
16	Telford			
48	34	Birmingham		
51	56	29	Worcester	
32	31	64	33	Ludlow

(a) Write down the distance between Shrewsbury and Birmingham.

....

(b) Ann drives from Telford to Worcester. She then drives from Worcester to Ludlow. Finally, she drives back from Ludlow to Telford. Work out the total distance that she drives.

....

....

3 This chart shows the distances, in miles, between some cities.

Portsmouth			
189	Swansea		
260	264	Leeds	
445	428	224	Glasgow

(a) Write down the distance between Portsmouth and Leeds.

....

(b) Emma drove from Portsmouth to Swansea, and then from Swansea to Glasgow. Faisal drove directly from Portsmouth to Glasgow. Work out how many more miles Emma travelled than Faisal.

....

....

Had a go ☐ Nearly there ☐ Nailed it! ☐

Routes

1 Joshua wants to go on three rides. The rides he wants to go on are the rollercoaster, the pirate ship and the log flume.

The diagram shows part of a theme park and the distances between the rides in metres.

Joshua uses the diagram to plan his route. His plan must start and end at the family area.

Plan the shortest route possible.

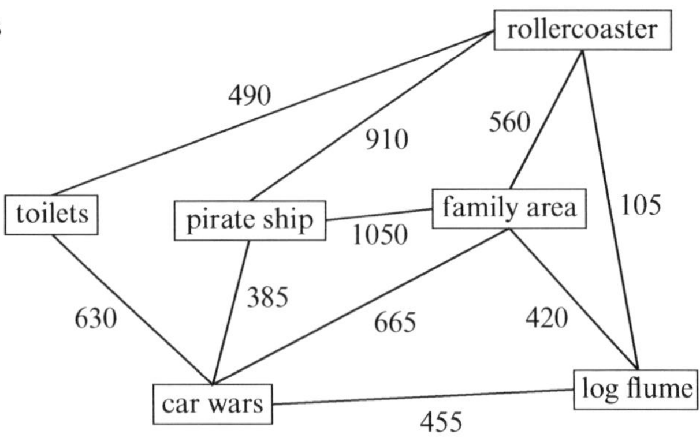

family area to the log flume to ....

....

2 Anjali has an appointment at the hospital at 10:40. On the way, she will stop at the florist for 5 minutes and the supermarket for 20 minutes. The map shows the time in minutes it will take Anjali to cycle between destinations.

What time will she need to leave to make sure she gets to the hospital on time?

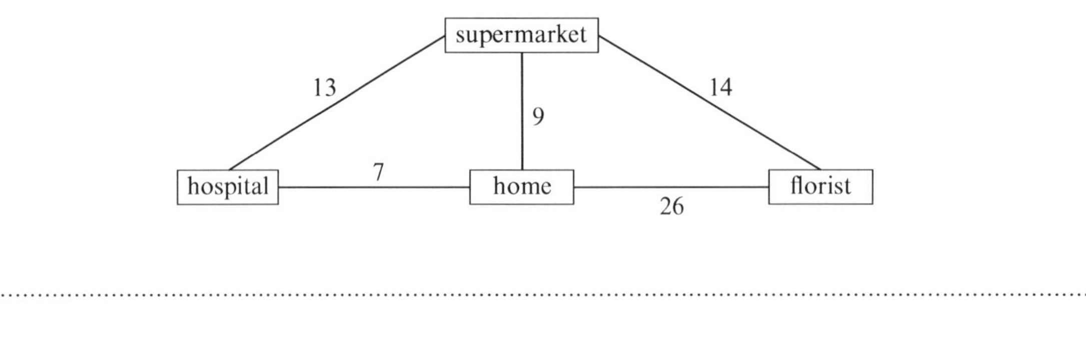

....

....

3 Abraham is a manager for a construction company. He needs to visit three different building sites: Ashton, Baggeridge and Conway. He will start from his office, visit Baggeridge first and finish back at the office.

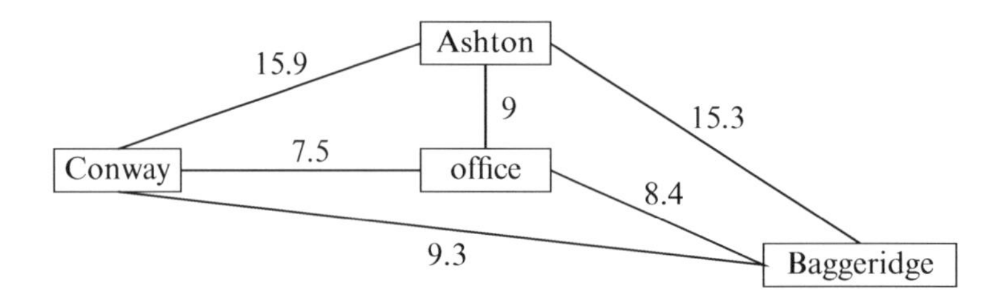

The diagram shows the different building sites and the distance between them in miles. Abraham does not want to travel more than 45 miles to visit the three sites. Find the shortest route for Abraham.

....

....

Length

GUIDED **1** Complete the table below showing the conversion factors for these units.

mm ⟶ cm	÷ 10	cm ⟶ mm	
cm ⟶ m		m ⟶ cm	× 100
m ⟶ km		km ⟶ m	

GUIDED **2** Convert these values to the units stated:

Kilo means one thousand.

(a) 35 mm to cm 35 ÷ ....

(b) 83 cm to mm ....

(c) 4.6 km to m ....

(d) 3900 m to km ....

3 Order these lengths from smallest to largest: 8000 mm 80 cm 80 m

....

4 Find the total of these lengths, in millimetres.

(a) 340 cm, 3.8 m and 14000 mm

....

(b) 3.2 km, 42.5 cm and 1780 mm

....

5 How many edgings of length 65 cm can fit along a path of length 9.1 m?

....

....

6 A book shelf is 1.6 m wide. Saskia wants to place a set of books across the shelf. She has 30 books. Each book is 53 mm wide. Will she have enough space for all the books?

Show your working and then write a conclusion.

....

....

....

Had a go ☐ Nearly there ☐ Nailed it! ☐

Weight

1 Complete the table below showing the conversion factors for these units.

kg ⟶ g	× 1000	g ⟶ kg	
g ⟶ mg		mg ⟶ g	÷ 1000

GUIDED **2** Convert these amounts to the units stated:

(a) 6.2 kg to g 6.2 × ....

(b) 5800 g to kg ....

(c) 640 mg to g ....

(d) 586 g to kg ....

3 Order these units of weight from smallest to largest:

400 000 mg 40 000 g 4 kg

....

4 Find the total of these weights, in grams.

(a) 2.4 kg, 850 g and 4500 mg

....

(b) 37 000 mg, 0.75 kg and 9400 g

....

5 How many 175 g clay ornaments can be made from a piece of clay weighing 3.5 kg?

Convert 3.5 kg into g

....

6 Henry is sending a package. It can have a maximum weight of 5 kg. He puts three parcels into the package. The parcels weigh 2.6 kg, 1500 g and 850 000 mg.

Will the package exceed the maximum weight?

Show your working and then write a conclusion.

....

....

Capacity

GUIDED **1** Complete the table below showing the conversion factors for these units.

litres ⟶ centilitres	× 100	centilitres ⟶ litres	
centilitres ⟶ millilitres		millilitres ⟶ centilitres	
litres ⟶ millilitres		millilitres ⟶ litres	÷ ....

GUIDED **2** Convert these amounts to the units stated:

(a) 8.3 litres to centilitres 8.3 litres × .... = ... g

(b) 7.6 litres to millilitres ....

(c) 640 millilitres to litres ....

(d) 780 centilitres to litres ....

3 Order these units of capacity from smallest to largest:

6 litres 63 500 millilitres 6300 centilitres

....

4 Find the total of these volumes, in centilitres.

(a) 6.9 centilitres, 7940 millilitres and 4.2 litres

....

(b) 3000 millilitres, 450 centilitres and 4.6 litres

....

5 How many 75 ml glasses can be filled from a bottle holding 4.5 litres of juice?

Convert 4.5 litres into millilitres.

....

6 A water tank has a volume of 120 litres. The water tank is filled from empty at a rate of 150 ml per second. How long will it take the water tank to fill? Give your answer in minutes and seconds.

....

....

Had a go ☐ Nearly there ☐ Nailed it! ☐

Money

GUIDED **1** Convert the following into pence.

(a) £0.38 0.38 × 100 = ...

(b) £152.89 ....

GUIDED **2** Convert the following into pounds.

(a) 967p 967 × 100 = £ ....

(b) 78 216p ....

3 Work out these calculations.

(a) 45p + £3.62 + £4.15 ....

(b) £10 − £2.63 – 69p ....

4 Albert goes shopping and buys a newspaper for £2.90, three bags of nuts at 89p each and four cartons of juice at 67p each. He pays with a £10 note.

How much change should he get?

....

5 Here is part of Laura's electricity bill.

units used: 3342
standing charge: £25.50 per quarter
cost: 4p per unit

Remember to give your answer to 2 decimal places as you are working in pounds and pence.

Work out the cost of the electricity bill.

....

....

....

6 Gary's Groceries and Bob's Store both sell cartons of yoghurts.

Gary's Groceries	Bob's Store
5 for £3.25	8 for £5.60

At which shop are cartons of yoghurts better value for money?

....

....

....

Temperature

1 These thermometers measure temperature in degrees Celsius. Write the temperatures they show.

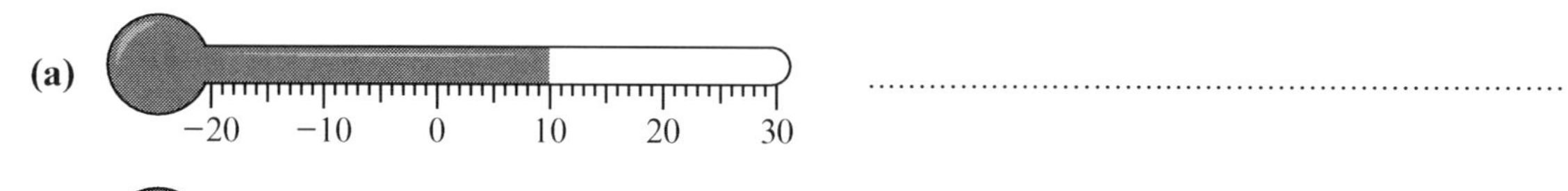

(a) ....

(b) ....

2 These thermometers measure temperature in degrees Celsius. Shade them so that they read:

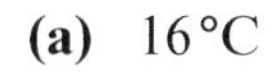

(a) 16 °C

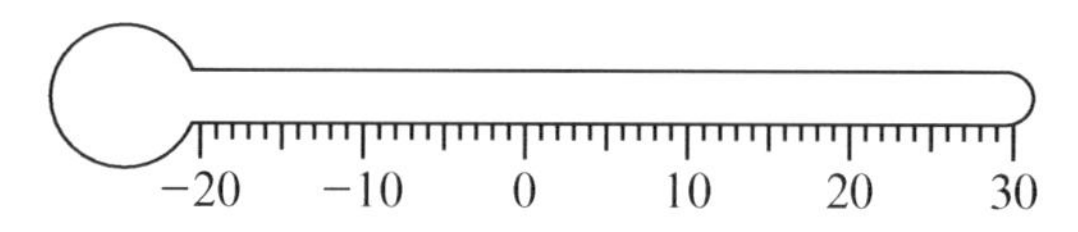

(b) −12 °C

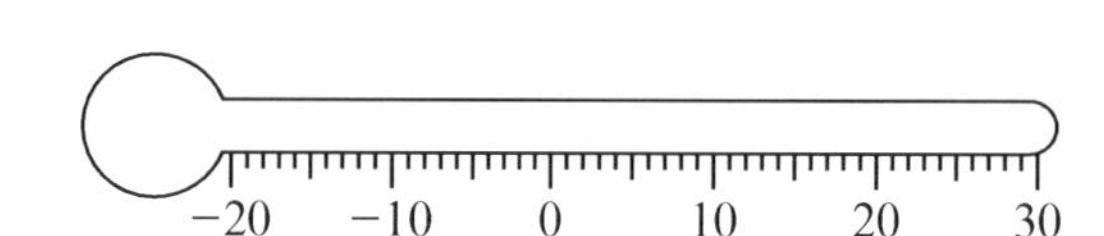

3 The table shows the temperatures in four cities at midnight one day.

City	Copenhagen	Berlin	Melbourne	Moscow
Temperature	−15 °C	−7 °C	7 °C	−19 °C

(a) Write down the highest temperature. ....

(b) Work out the difference in temperature between Copenhagen and Melbourne.

....

(c) At 6 p.m., the temperature in Berlin was 4 degrees higher than the temperature at midnight.

Work out the temperature in Berlin at 6 p.m.

....

4 The temperature at 12 noon is 8 °C but by 6 p.m. it has dropped by 10 degrees. By 9 p.m. it has dropped a further 6 degrees and by 12 midnight it has dropped a further 7 degrees.

Work out the temperature at:

(a) 6 p.m. ....

(b) 9 p.m. ....

(c) 12 midnight ....

(d) What was the overall drop in temperature from 12 noon to 12 midnight?

....

Had a go ☐ Nearly there ☐ Nailed it! ☐

Perimeter and area

1 Two shapes have been drawn on centimetre-squared paper.
Find the area and perimeter of each shape.

Count the shaded squares to find the area.

(a)

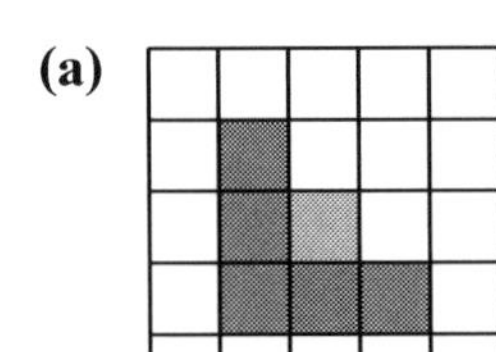

area = ...

perimeter = ...

(b)

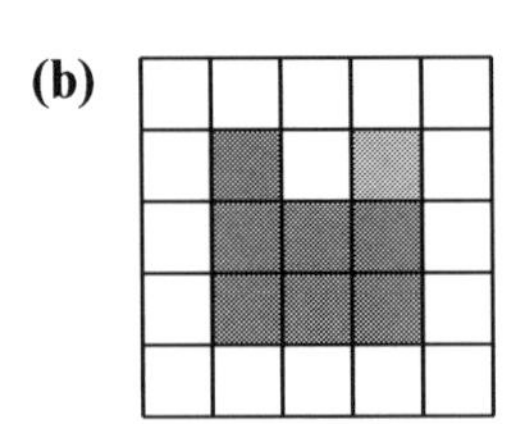

area = ...

perimeter = ...

Count around the shape to find the perimeter.

2 Two shapes have been drawn on centimetre-squared paper.
Estimate the area of each shape.

Count 1 cm² for every whole square and every part square that is more than half shaded. Count 0.5 cm² for every half square.

(a)

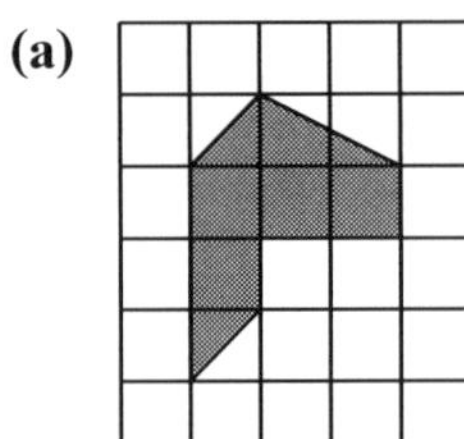

area of whole squares = ...

area of part squares ≈ ....

total area ≈ .... + ... = ...

(b)

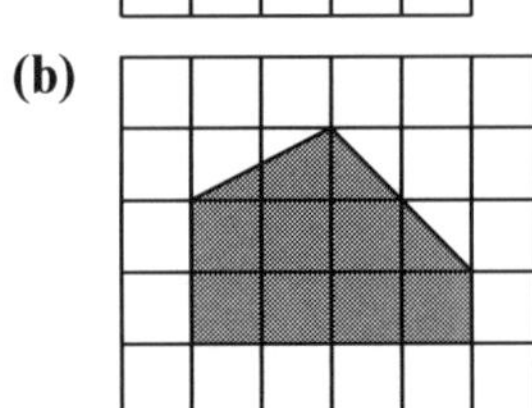

....

....

....

3 Work out the perimeter of each shape.

(a)

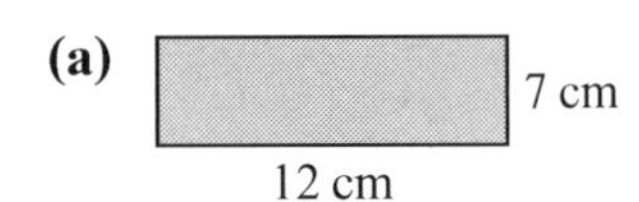

....

(b) 15 cm

8 cm 8 cm

6 cm

....

Area of rectangles

1 Find the area of each rectangle.

area of rectangle = length × width

(a) 12 cm

7 cm

....

(b) 8 m

3 m

....

2 Use the areas of these rectangles to work out the lengths of the unknown sides.

(a) area = 112 cm^2

14 cm

?

missing length = 112 ÷ 14 = ...

(b) area = 221 m^2

?

13 m

....

3 This diagram shows the plan of a grazing field for sheep.

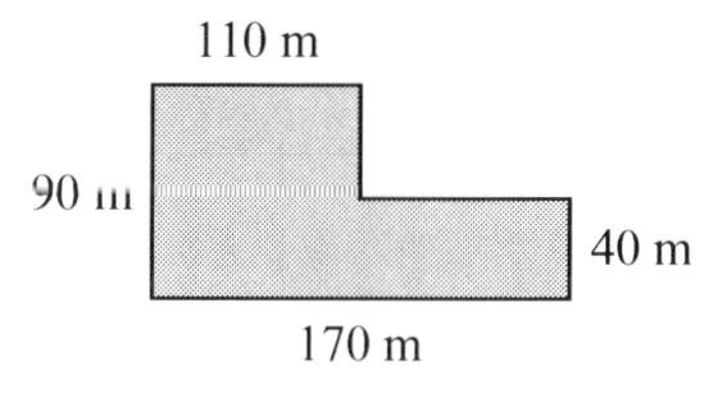

Split the shape into two rectangles.

Each sheep needs 500 m^2 of grazing area.

Work out how many sheep can graze in this field.

....

....

4 This diagram shows the floor of a warehouse.

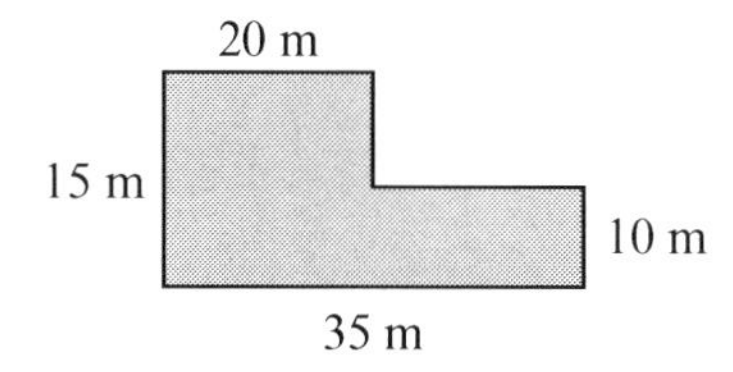

The manager needs to polish the floor. One tin of polish will cover 15 m^2 of floor and costs £20.

The manager has £500 to spend on polish. Has she got enough money to buy the polish for the floor?

....

....

Had a go ☐ **Nearly there** ☐ **Nailed it!** ☐

Problem-solving practice

GUIDED **1** Leon bought the following items from a shop: two pens at £2.75 each, four pencils at 49p each and a pack of envelopes for £3.95. He paid with a £10 note and £5 note.

How much change did he get?

cost = (2 × 2.75) + (4 × ....

....

2 The diagram shows a man standing next to a tree.

The man is of average height.

The man and the tree are drawn to same scale.

(a) Write down an estimate for the height,

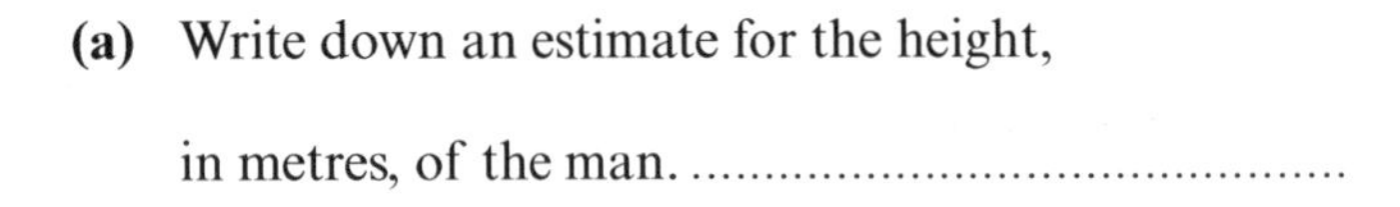

in metres, of the man. ....

(b) Work out an estimate for the height,

in metres, of the tree. ....

3 A pack of 9 toilet rolls costs £5.40. A pack of 4 toilet rolls costs £2.60

Which pack gives better value for money? You must show all your working.

....

....

....

4 The total weight of five metal balls is shown on this weighing scale.

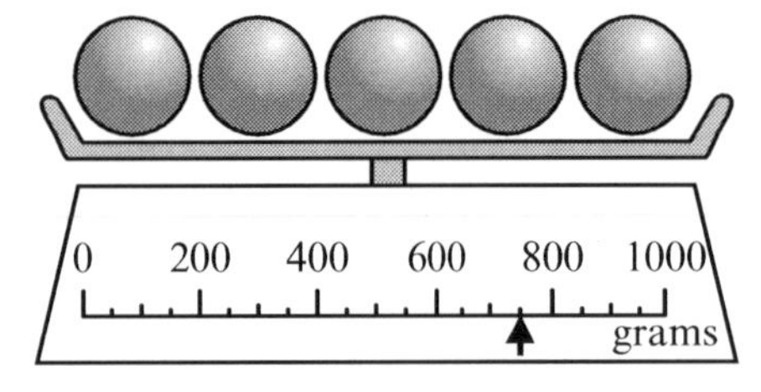

Each metal ball has the same weight. Work out the weight of one metal ball.

....

....

Problem-solving practice

1 The diagram shows the distances in miles between some towns along an old Roman road.

Nuneaton —16— Tamworth —69— Oswestry —13— Llangollen —54— Bangor

Using the information shown in the diagram, complete the table.

Bangor				
	Llangollen			
		Nuneaton		
67	13		Oswestry	
		16	69	Tamworth

2 Edward is a delivery driver for an electrical store. The electrical store is in Alton. On Monday, Edward has to deliver some electrical goods in Boswell, Carlton and Denton.

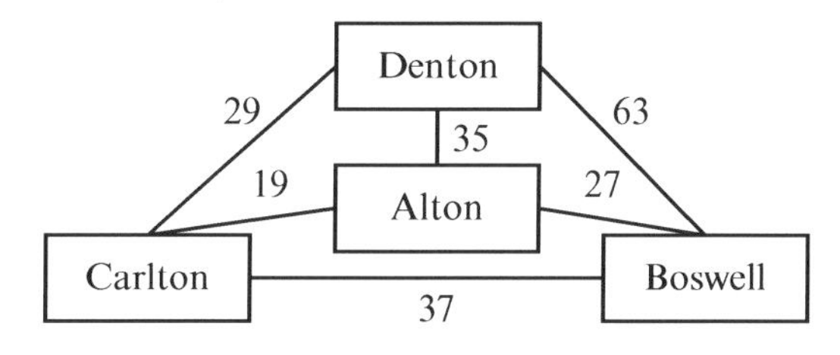

Edward needs to start and finish in Alton. He wants to take the shortest route possible.
The diagram shows the distances, in kilometres, between the towns.

Find a route for Edward and work out the total distance of the route.

....

....

Problem-solving practice

1 Lewis buys a cottage. The lawn in his back garden is in the shape of a rectangle. The lawn has a length of 15 m and a width of 12 m.

Lewis wants to buy scallop edgings for his lawn. Each scallop edging is 60 cm long. The total length of the scallop edgings must be equal to the perimeter of the lawn. Each scallop edging costs £1.75

What is the total cost of the scallop edgings?

Find the perimeter.

....

....

....

2 Here is a diagram of part of a wall in David's house.

David is going to cover this part of the wall with square tiles.
The square tiles have sides of 40 cm.

Work out the number of tiles David needs.

3.2 m

2.4 m

....

....

....

3 The diagram shows the floor plan of Simran's conservatory. Simran is going to cover the floor with tiles.

The tiles are sold in packs.
One pack of tiles will cover $2\,m^2$.

A pack of tiles normally costs £29.50
She can get a discount of 50% off the cost of the tiles.

Simran has £180. Does she have enough money to buy all the tiles she needs? You must show all your working.

6 m

2 m

5 m

2 m

....

....

....

Symmetry

1 On the shapes below, draw:

(a) one line of symmetry

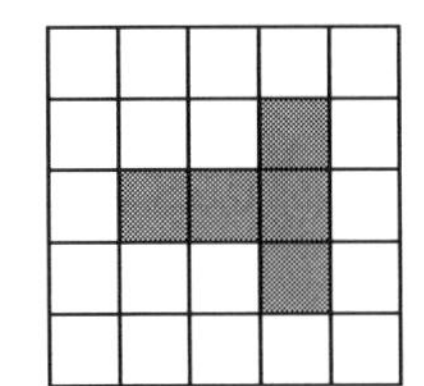

(b) two lines of symmetry.

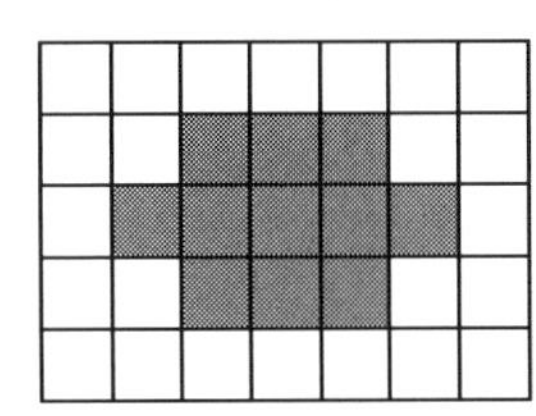

2 Here are some shapes.

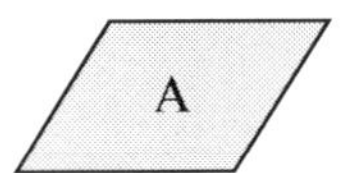

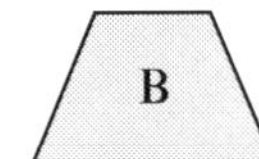

Write down the letter of a shape that has:

(a) no lines of symmetry ....

(b) exactly one line of symmetry ....

(c) exactly two lines of symmetry. ....

3 On the diagrams below, shade one square so that the shape has:

(a) exactly one line of symmetry

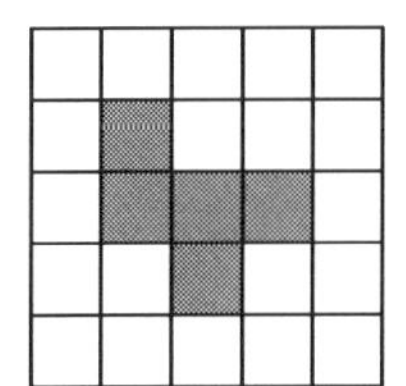

(b) rotational symmetry of order 2

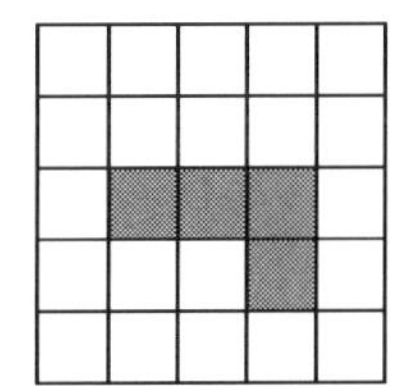

(c) exactly one line of symmetry

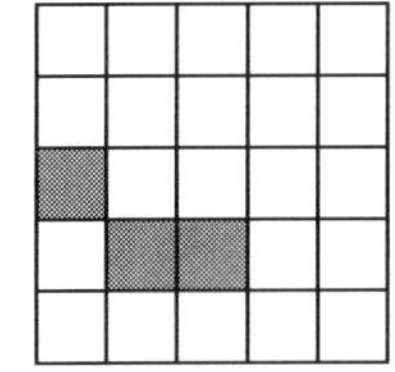

(d) rotational symmetry of order 2

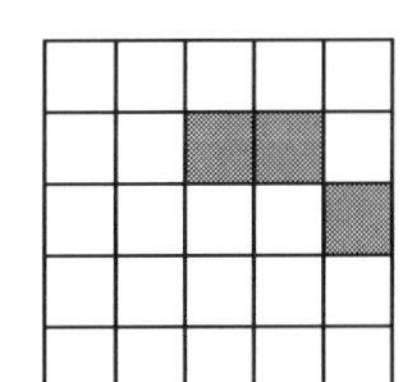

Properties of 2D shapes

GUIDED 1 Draw a line connecting each shape to its name.

rectangle kite parallelogram rhombus square

GUIDED 2 Complete this table by drawing an example of a regular and irregular shape.

Name of shape	Regular	Irregular	Name of shape	Regular	Irregular
triangle			hexagon		
quadrilateral			octagon		

3 The floor in Emma's conservatory is a rectangle that is 4.5 m long by 3 m wide. She wants to cover the floor completely with tiles. Each tile is a square with sides of length 25 cm.

(a) How many tiles will she need?

....

....

(b) A box contains 18 tiles. Each box costs £27.50. Emma has £300 to spend. Does she have enough money to tile the floor? Give a reason for your answer.

....

....

....

Scale drawings and maps

1 The lines below are drawn to scale. Work out the actual lengths they represent by using the scales.

Measure the length of the line in cm, then multiply to find the right answer.

(a) scale = 1 cm to 5 m

______________ ....

(b) scale = 1 mm to 8 km

___________ ....

2 A and B are points on an island.

The scale of the map is 1 mm to 4 km.

Find the real distance, in kilometres, between A and B.

A

B

....

3 The scale of a map is 1 : 20 000
On the map, the distance between two cities is 25 cm.

Work out the real distance between the two cities. Give your answer in kilometres.

....

4 The Eiffel Tower is 300 metres tall. A scale model is made of the Eiffel Tower. The scale of the model is 1 : 200

Work out the height of the scale model. Give your answer in centimetres.

....

5 Here is a scale plan of Geoffrey's shop floor where 1 cm represents 2 m. He wants to cover the shop floor using tiles. Each tile is square with sides of 25 cm.

Work out how many tiles Geoffrey needs.

....

....

Had a go ☐ Nearly there ☐ Nailed it! ☐

Using plans

1 Robert is going to put a trampoline and a stool in his exercise room at home. The trampoline needs a rectangular floor space 200 cm by 100 cm. The trampoline must be at least 100 cm from the door and window. The stool needs a rectangular floor space 100 cm by 50 cm. The stool must be in the corner. He makes a plan of his exercise room.

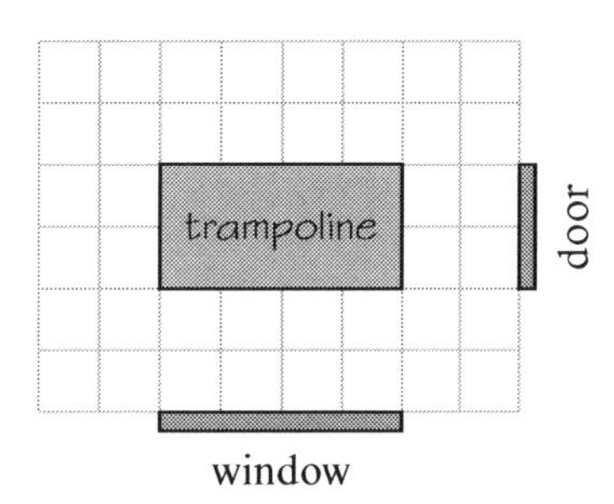

key: 1 square on the plan = 50 cm by 50 cm

Draw the trampoline and the stool on the plan.

2 Patsy wants to put a shed in her garden. The base of the shed is a rectangle that is 4 m long and 2 m wide. Patsy wants the shed to be at least 3 m from the house and to be at least 3 m from the wall. She has a plan of the garden.

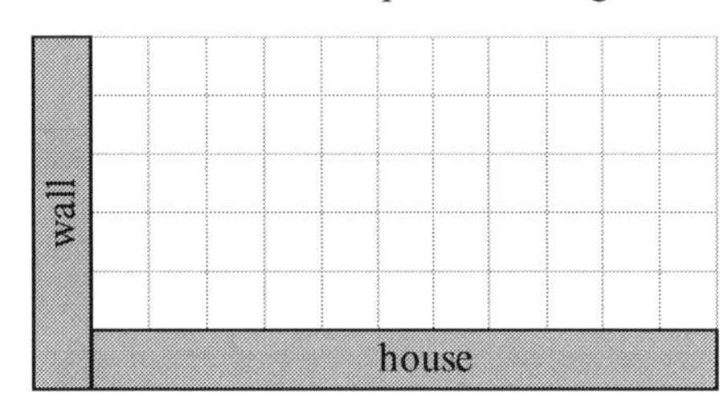

key: 1 square on the plan = 1 m in the garden

Draw where the shed could be positioned on Patsy's plan.

3 Tom wants a bench and a table for his workroom. He draws a plan of the room, on centimetre-squared paper. The bench is 200 cm long and 100 cm wide. It needs a rectangular floor space. Tom wants to put the bench along the wall opposite the cupboard. The table is 150 cm by 100 cm. It needs a rectangular floor space. The table needs to be at least 100 cm away from the cupboard.

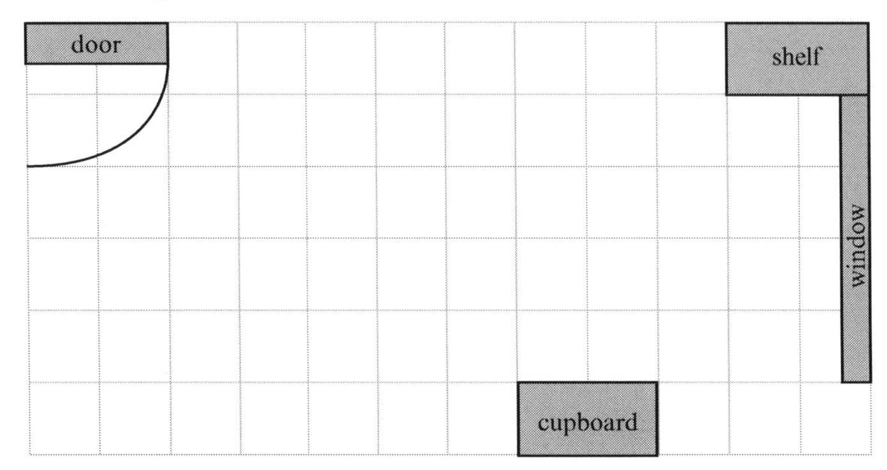

key: 1 cm on the grid = 50 cm in the workroom

Draw the bench and the table on the plan.

Angles

1 Draw a line from the name of each angle to the correct diagram.

acute obtuse reflex

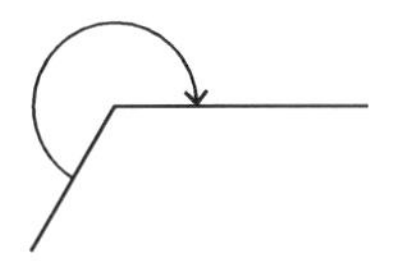

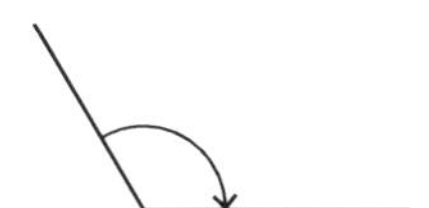

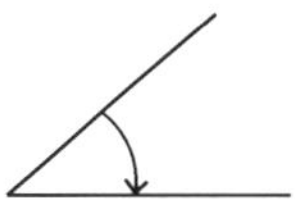

2 Use the diagrams to answer the questions below and give a reason for your answer.

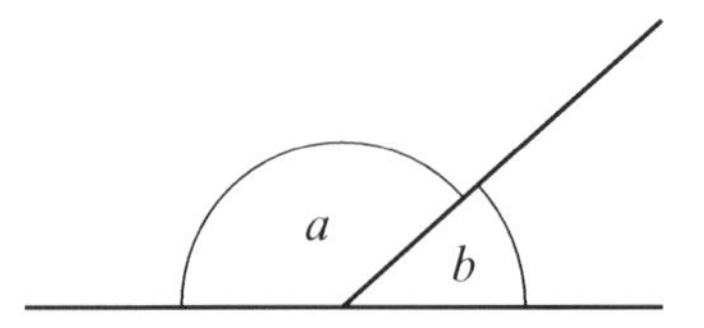

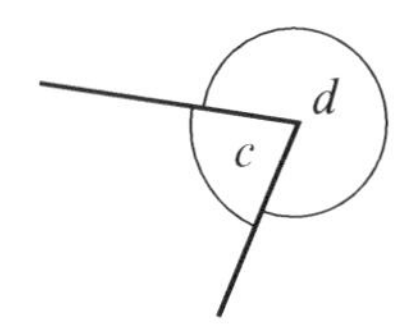

(a) What type of angle is a?

....

(b) What type of angle is d?

....

3 Estimate the size of these angles.

(a)

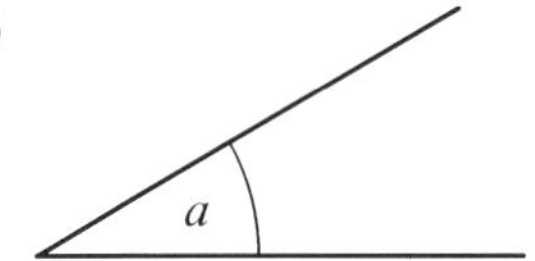

(b)

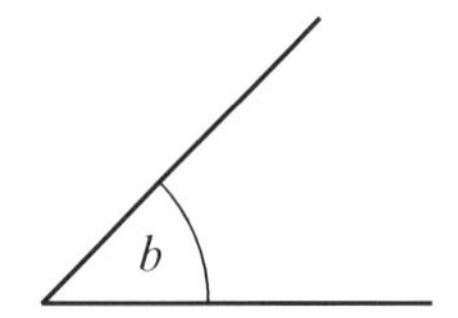

....

4 Use a protractor to measure all of the angles in each shape.

(a)

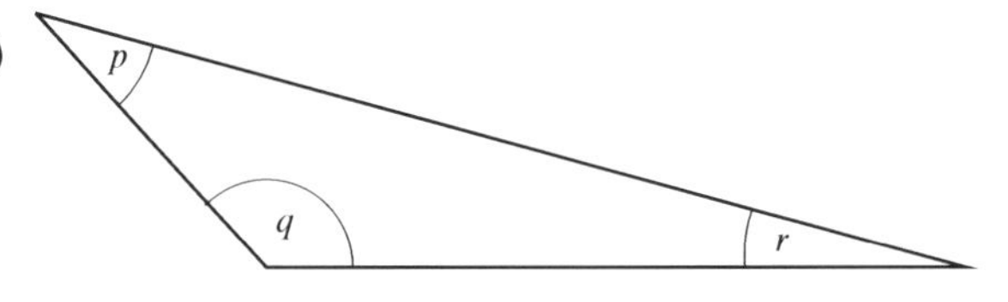

p = ...

q = 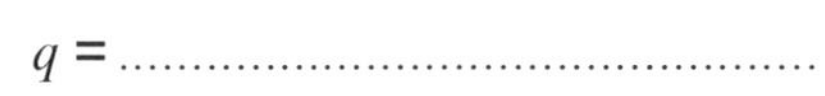

r = 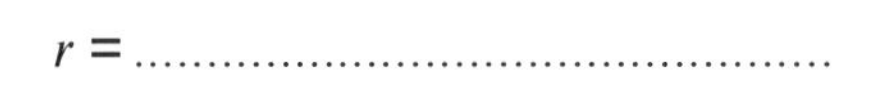

(b)

e = 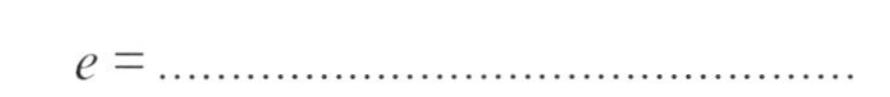

f = 

g = ...

h = ...

Problem-solving practice

1 This diagram shows two places on a map.

× tower

scale: 1 mm represents 5 miles.

×
hill

> Use a ruler to measure the distance between the hill and the tower.

What is the real distance, in miles, from the hill to the tower?

....

2 Chrissie is buying ceiling tiles for her office. The office is 7 m long and 8 m wide.

Chrissie sees these two advertisements for ceiling tiles.

> Work out the area of Chrissie's office to help you find out how many packs of tiles she would need to buy from each shop.

Handyware Mansion ceiling tiles £45.00 per pack covers 10 square metres	Do It Yourself Hypermarket 1 m by 1 m ceiling tiles £19.00 for a pack of four

Chrissie wants to spend as little as possible. From which shop should she buy the ceiling tiles?

....

....

....

....

3 Chris made a scale model of a car to a scale of 1 : 15

The height of the model car is 9 cm.

(a) Work out the height of the real car. Give your answer in metres.

....

(b) The length of the real car is 4.95 m. Work out the length of the model car. Give your answer in centimetres.

....

Problem-solving practice

1 Karen is going to soundproof the floor in the music room. The diagram shows the shape of the music room.

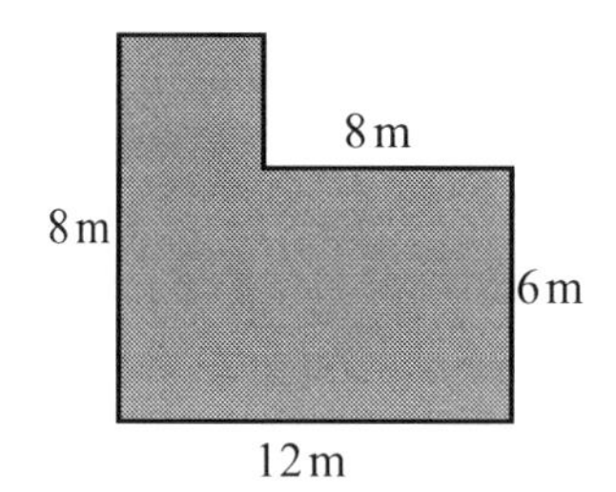

She is going to cover the entire floor.

She can choose either rubber mats or vinyl floor tiles.

Each rubber mat is square with sides of length 40 cm.

They come in packs of 50

Each vinyl floor tile is rectangular with length 1 m and width 50 cm. They come in packs of 20

She only wants to use one type of flooring to soundproof her floor and she wants to buy as few packs as possible.

Which type of flooring should she use?

....

....

....

....

2 Sharon wants to put a small bed and a rug in her baby's bedroom.

Split the shape into two rectangles.

The small bed needs a rectangular floor space 150 cm by 75 cm. It must be at least 25 cm from the window and at least 50 cm from the radiator.

The rug needs a square floor space 100 cm by 100 cm and it must not touch the radiator.

Sharon draws a plan of the floor on a grid.

Key: 1 square on the grid is 25 cm by 25 cm on the floor

Draw the small bed and the rug on the plan.

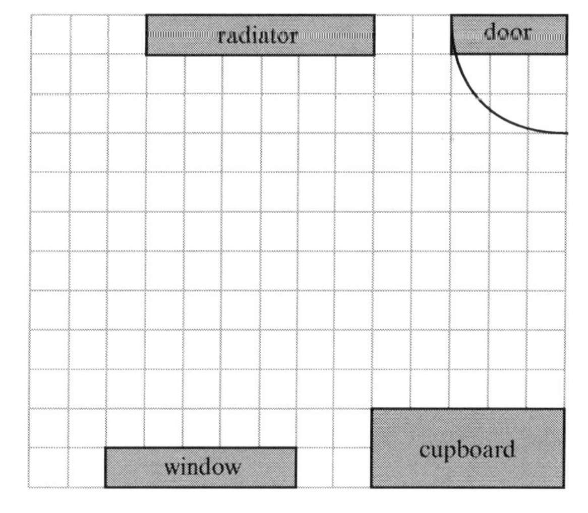

Tables

GUIDED **1** The table gives information about the entrance prices, in £, for a safari park.

	November to March	April to October
adults	£6.70	£10.40
children (under 16)	£3.80	£5.80
family (2 adults and 2 children)	£16.90	£26.40

(a) In February, how much more does it cost an adult than a child to visit the park?

£6.70 − £3.80 = ...

(b) Four children have £65 to spend. They plan to visit the park in their summer holidays. How much would they have left to spend on food after they bought their tickets?

....

(c) What is the difference in cost for a family with two adults and three children to visit the park in January rather than July?

....

2 Corey works at a garden centre in the summer holidays. He earns £7.40 for each hour he works. The table shows the hours he worked in August.

Week	1	2	3	4
Number of hours	35	37	36	31

Corey thinks he earned more than £1,000 in August. Is he correct?

....

3 Josh needs to buy a new shower unit, tray and glass enclosure for his bathroom. He wants to buy them all from the same online shop. He finds these prices on the internet.

Item	**Showers4U**	**Wackes**	**C & R**
shower unit (£)	453.95	330.99	474.89
tray (£)	315.99	382.49	375.00
glass enclosure (£)	397.65	373.35	359.63
delivery charge (£)	17.95	18.99	14.99

Josh wants to pay as little as possible for the shower fittings. How much will the new shower fittings cost including the delivery charge?

....

....

Tally charts and frequency tables

1 James has a farm. The incomplete table gives information about the number of animals on his farm.

Animal	cows	hens	pigs	sheep
Tally	𝍸 𝍸 𝍸 III	𝍸 𝍸 IIII		𝍸 III
Frequency			11	

(a) Complete the tally and frequency columns on the table.

Remember that 𝍸 represents 5

(b) How many hens are there on the farm? ....

(c) How many animals did James have on his farm in total?

....

2 Employees of a retail store were asked how they travel to work. The results are shown below.

bus, car, walk, bus, car, bus, bike, walk, bus, bus, car, walk, walk, car, bike, bus, walk, bus, bus, car, walk, bus, car, walk, bus, bus, bike, bus, walk, walk

Method of travel	bike	bus	car	walk
Tally				
Frequency				

(a) Complete the table.

(b) Which was the most popular method of travel? ....

(c) How many more travelled by bus than by car?

....

3 The table shows information about 102 vehicles on a ferry.

Type of vehicle	car	coach	motorhome	lorry
Frequency		26		

There are twice as many cars as coaches. There are equal numbers of motorhomes as lorries.

Complete the table.

Data collection sheets

1 Sara recorded the colour of each car going past her college one morning.
Here are her results: white, white, black, blue, white, red, red, blue, red, blue, black, white, black, white, blue, white, red, red, white, red

(a) Design and complete a data collection sheet to collect this information.

Colour	black	blue		
Tally	III			
Frequency	3			

(b) What was the most common colour of car in her results?

....

(c) Work out the total number of cars.

....

2 Sandra works in a library. She needs to record how many books are borrowed one day. She also wants to record how many hours the library is open each day.

Design a data collection sheet to collect this information.

3 Kim plans a dinner for a fundraising event. She needs to know the menu choices for each table at the dinner. People can have:

starter: soup or pate main: curry or lasagne dessert: ice cream or cheesecake

Kim needs a data collection sheet for each table. Each sheet must have space to record the table number and how many people chose each option.

Design a data collection sheet for Kim to use.

Reading bar charts

GUIDED **1** Mrs Patel asked the students in her class which type of pets they had. The bar chart shows some information about the results from her class.

Write down two things that are wrong with the bar chart.

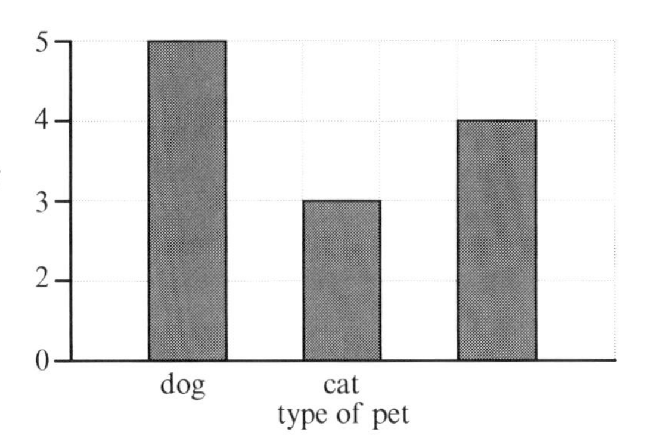

1 On the vertical axis ....

....

2 ....

....

2 The bar chart shows the numbers of different toys sold on one Friday at Miguel's Toy shop.

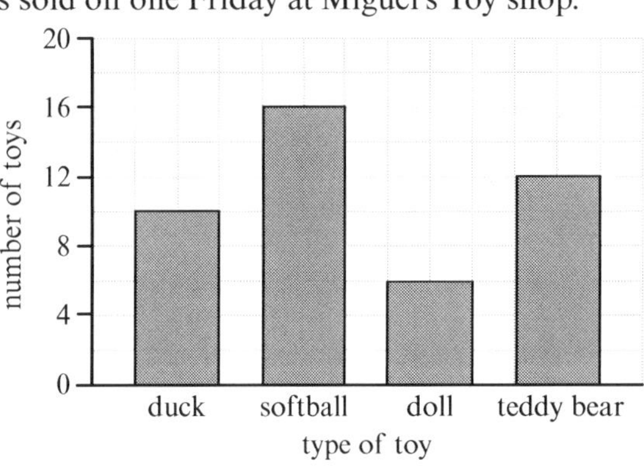

(a) How many softballs did he sell?

....

(b) How many more ducks than dolls were sold?

....

(c) How many toys were sold altogether?

....

3 The bar chart shows the number of times a song was downloaded from a website in one week.

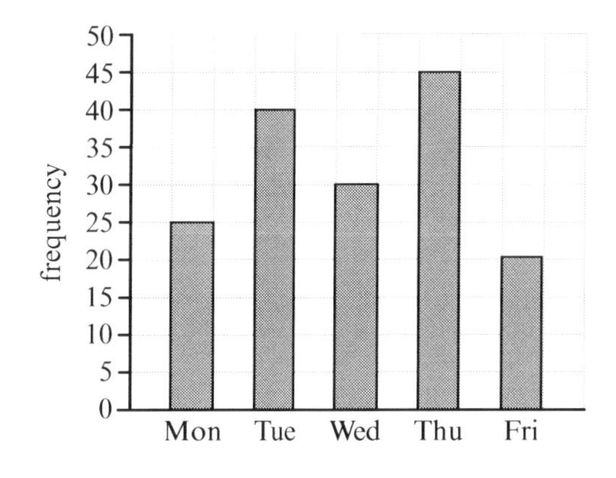

(a) How many times was the song downloaded on Monday?

....

(b) On which day was it downloaded most times?

....

(c) What is the difference in the number of times it was downloaded on Tuesday and Friday?

....

(d) How many times was the song downloaded during the week?

....

Reading pictograms

GUIDED **1** This pictogram shows information about the number of loaves sold over five days in a bakery.

Key: [loaf] means 10 loaves

Monday	
Tuesday	
Wednesday	
Thursday	
Friday	

(a) How many loaves were sold on Monday?

4 × ....

(b) On which day did the bakery sell the fewest loaves?

....

2 This pictogram shows information about the numbers of milkshakes of different flavours sold by a cafe one afternoon.

banana	
raspberry	
chocolate	
strawberry	
toffee	

(a) Which was the most popular flavour of milkshake?

....

(b) The shop sold 30 raspberry milkshakes. How many milkshakes does each whole symbol represent?

....

3 The pictogram gives information about the number of chocolate eggs sold from a shop each day from Monday to Thursday.

Key: [egg] means 8 eggs

Monday	
Tuesday	
Wednesday	
Thursday	

(a) How many more eggs were sold on Thursday than were sold on Wednesday?

....

(b) How many eggs in total were sold over the four days?

....

Reading pie charts

1 The pie chart shows information about the types of fish Simon caught in one year.

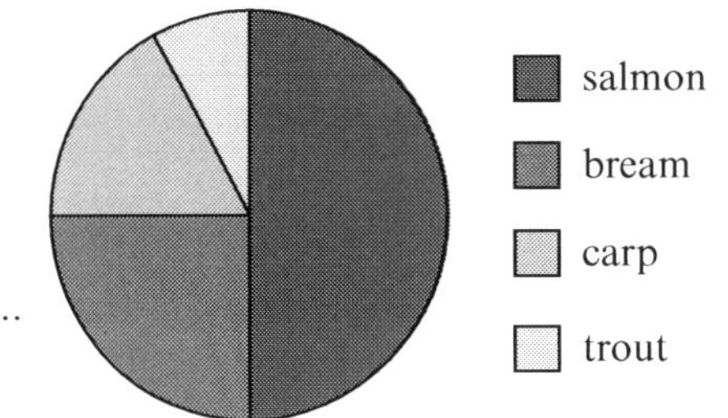

(a) Which fish did Simon catch the most of?

....

(b) What fraction of the fish he caught were bream?

....

(c) Simon caught 28 bream. How many fish did he catch in total?

....

2 The pie charts show information about the eye colour of a number of children in two schools.

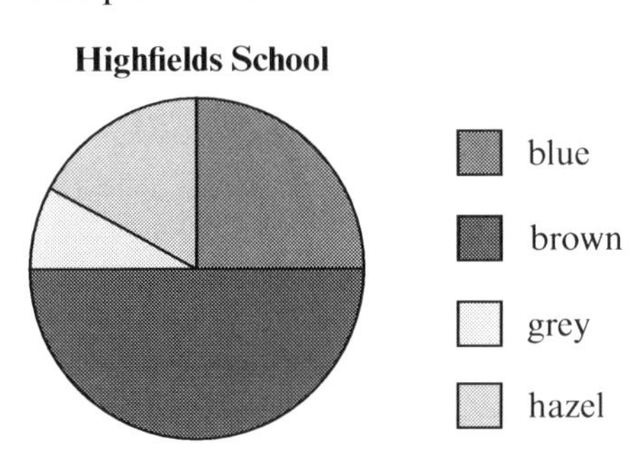

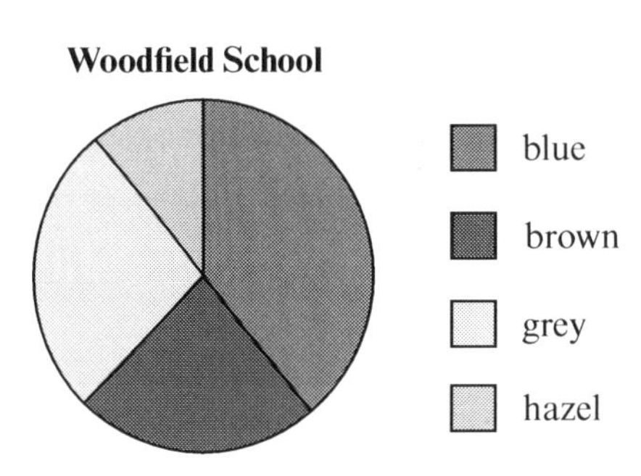

(a) What colour was the most common at Woodfield School?

....

(b) 120 children at Highfields School had brown eyes. How many children had blue eyes?

....

(c) 'There were more children with hazel eyes at Woodfield School than at Highfields School.'

Is this statement true? Explain your reasons.

....

3 Simon and Taran are in a chess club. The pie charts show information about the number of games Simon and Taran each won last year. They also show information about the number of games Simon and Taran each lost last year.

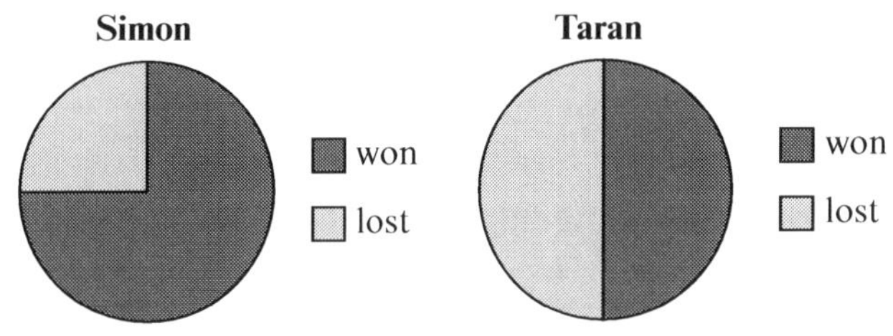

Simon played 64 games. Taran played 102 games. Who won more games and by how many?

....

Had a go ☐ Nearly there ☐ Nailed it! ☐

Reading line graphs

1 Ian uses this graph to convert between gallons and litres.

There are 40 litres of diesel in the tank of lorry A.

There are 8 gallons of diesel in the tank of lorry B.

Which lorry has more diesel in its tank?

....

....

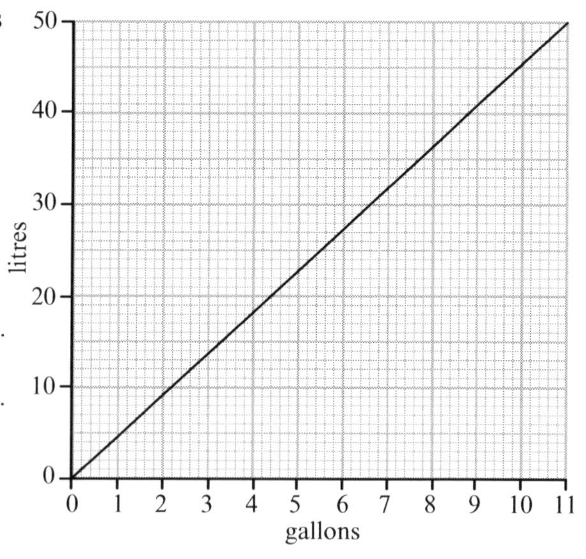

2 This graph can be used to convert between pounds and kilograms.

Asha's bag weighs 9 kilograms. Pam's bag weighs 18 pounds.

Whose bag weighs less?

....

....

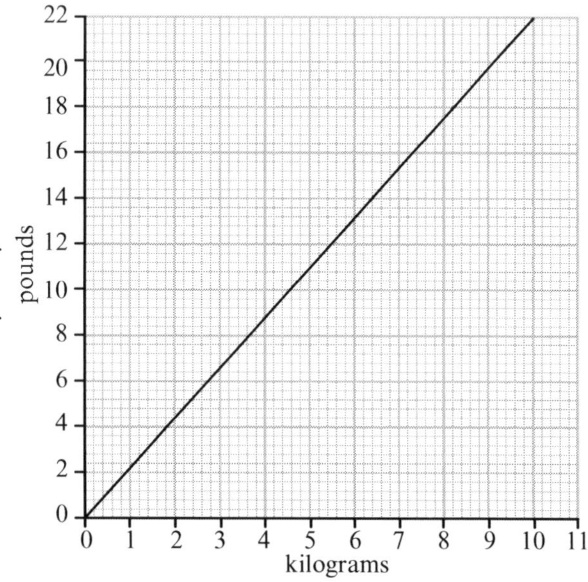

3 This graph shows the midday temperature in London measured each weekday for a week.

(a) What is the difference between the maximum temperature and the minimum temperature?

....

(b) Describe how the temperature changes between Wednesday and Friday.

....

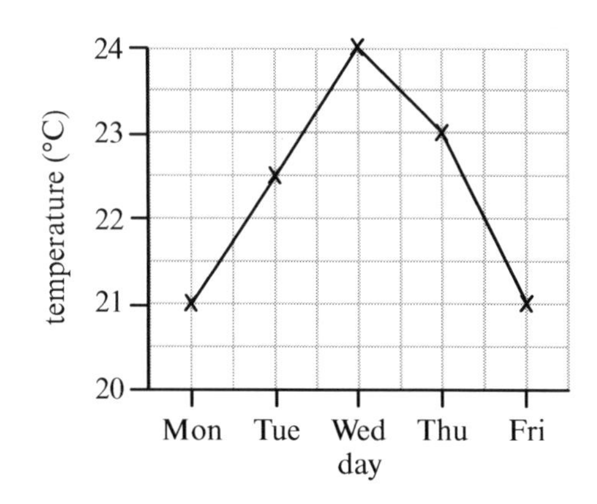

Planning a graph or chart

1 This table shows the average temperature in London for five months.

Month	Jan	Feb	Mar	Apr	May
Temperature (°C)	9	10	12	15	18

(a) Which data will be on the horizontal axis? ....

(b) Which data will be on the vertical axis? ....

(c) Your graph paper has 10 horizontal lines. What would be a suitable scale for the vertical axis?

The scale should go up in multiples of ....

(d) Which type of graph would you draw? ....

2 This table shows the profits of a company over a period of five weeks.

Week	1	2	3	4	5
Profit (£)	5,000	12,000	10,000	7,000	2,000

(a) Which data will be on the horizontal axis? ....

(b) Which data will be on the vertical axis? ....

(c) Your graph paper has 15 horizontal lines. What would be a suitable scale for the vertical axis?

....

(d) Which type of graph would you draw? ....

3 This table shows the number of cars rented from a garage each day for five days.

Day	Mon	Tue	Wed	Thu	Fri
Number of cars	16	23	19	12	32

(a) Which data will be on the horizontal axis? ....

(b) Which data will be on the vertical axis? ....

(c) Your graph paper has 20 horizontal lines. What would be a suitable scale for the vertical axis?

....

(d) Which type of graph would you draw? ....

Had a go ☐ Nearly there ☐ Nailed it! ☐

Drawing bar charts

1 The table shows Mark's profits for the first 6 months of the year.

Month	Jan	Feb	Mar	Apr	May	Jun
Profit (£)	1,000	1,200	1,300	1,450	1,600	1,650

Mark wants to show this information to his business partner. Draw a bar chart to show this information.

Draw the bars with an equal width and leave space between them. Remember to label the axes.

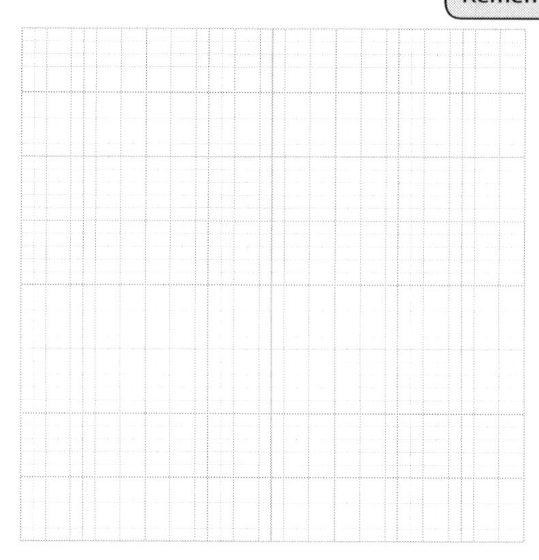

2 Raj is a freelance editor. He wants to plan a holiday for the summer. He wants to go in the month that he is likely to work the fewest hours. He creates this table of the hours he worked each month the previous summer. Draw a bar chart to show this information.

Month	Apr	May	Jun	Jul	Aug
Hours worked	100	80	125	70	100

Drawing pictograms

1 This pictogram shows the numbers of hours of sunshine in Helsinki on Monday, Tuesday and Wednesday of one week.

Monday	● ● ● ●
Tuesday	● ● ●
Wednesday	● ● ◖
Thursday	
Friday	

Key: ● represents 2 hours

(a) How many hours of sunshine were there on Tuesday?

....

(b) How many more hours of sunshine were there on Monday than Wednesday?

$4 \times 2 - 2.5 \times 2 =$ ....

(c) There were 7 hours of sunshine on Thursday. There were 4 hours of sunshine on Friday. Use this information to complete the pictogram.

2 This pictogram gives information about the numbers of packets of sweets sold by a shop some days in one week.

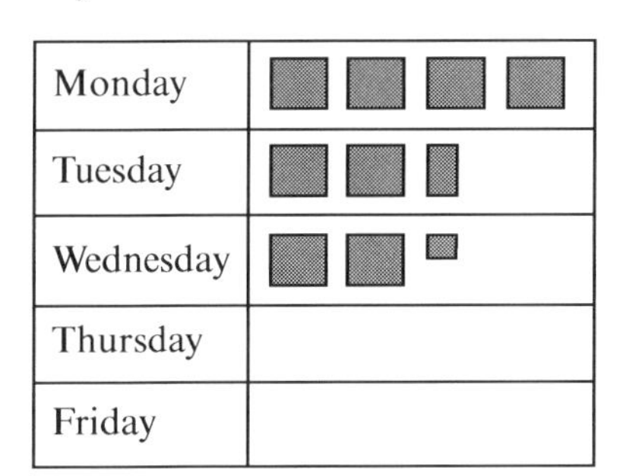

Key: ■ represents .... packets

(a) The total number of packets of sweets sold on Monday was 32. Complete the key.

(b) How many packets of sweets in total were sold on Tuesday and Wednesday?

....

(c) 36 packets of sweets were sold on Thursday. 10 packets of sweets were sold on Friday.
Use this information to complete the pictogram.

Drawing line graphs

1 This table shows the population of a town, rounded to the nearest thousand, after each census.

Year	1951	1961	1971	1981	1991	2001	2011
Population (thousands)	14	16	17	20	23	27	29

Draw a line graph to show this information.

Work out an appropriate scale for the axes and label them. Plot each point then join them together with straight lines.

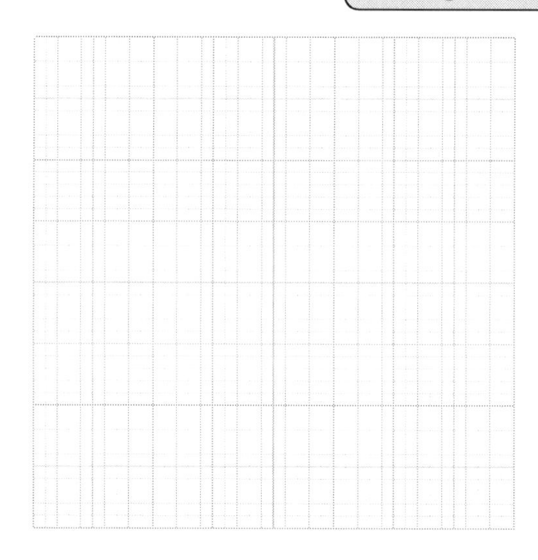

2 The table shows the value of a car over a period of seven years.

Year	2010	2011	2012	2013	2014	2015	2016
Value (£)	32,000	28,000	24,000	20,000	16,000	12,000	8,000

Draw a line graph to show this information.

Mean

1 In a survey, Sonia asked nine of her classmates how many foreign countries they had visited. Here are her results.

6 4 3 4 10 9 3 2 4

Work out the mean of her results.

Add up all the numbers and divide by how many there are.

6 + 4 + ...

2 Roy wants to give the plumbers at his company a pay rise. He will give them a pay rise if his mean monthly profit over the last 8 months is more than £7,250. This table shows the profit each month for the last 8 months.

Month	Feb	Mar	Apr	May	Jun	Jul	Aug	Sep
Profit (£)	7,410	6,750	8,400	7,300	9,650	4,025	7,050	8,175

Will Roy give the plumbers a pay rise? Show your working out.

....

3 Seven friends want to do the Three Peaks challenge for charity. They must raise a mean of at least £375 each before they do the challenge. Here are the amounts each friend has raised.

Name	Ali	Beth	Carl	Dal	Emma	Frank	Gary
Amount raised (£)	370	410	390	245	365	415	360

Can they do the Three Peaks challenge for charity? Show your working out.

....

4 This bar chart shows the price of 1 litre of petrol at 6 garages in Wolverhampton.

The UK mean price for 1 litre of petrol is 105.7p. Is the mean price per litre for these garages in Wolverhampton less than the UK mean price?

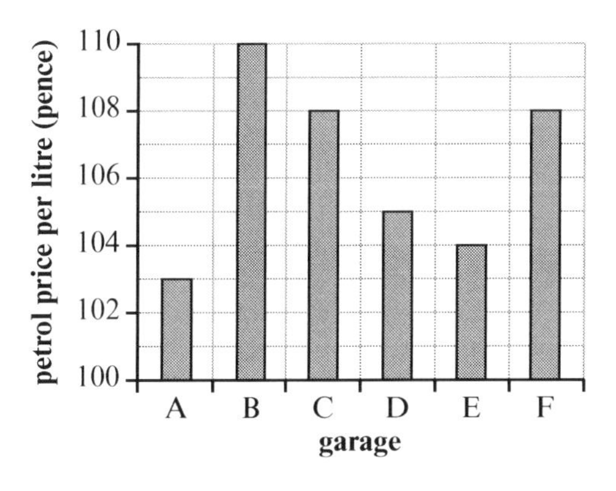

....

....

Had a go ☐ Nearly there ☐ Nailed it! ☐

Range

1 Nine people entered a dancing competition. Here are the number of points that each of the contestant scored.

14 5 4 11 5 2 15 7 9

Work out the range of scores achieved.

range = highest value – lowest value

....

2 Trainee apprentices in carpentry and retail took an aptitude test. Here are the results.

Carpentry	14	19	13	15	14	15	15	17
Retail	14	17	14	14	12	15		

The tutor says, 'The range of the carpentry marks is 1 bigger than the range of the retail marks.' Is the tutor correct? Show your working.

....

....

3 This table shows the midday temperature on each day for nine days in a factory.

Day	1	2	3	4	5	6	7	8	9
Temperature (°C)	23	24	22	20	23	26	24	23	28

Find the range of temperatures.

....

4 For a quality control inspection, Tim has to check the number of screws in five boxes. All the boxes are the same size. The bar chart shows the number of screws in five different boxes. Work out the range for the number of screws in a box.

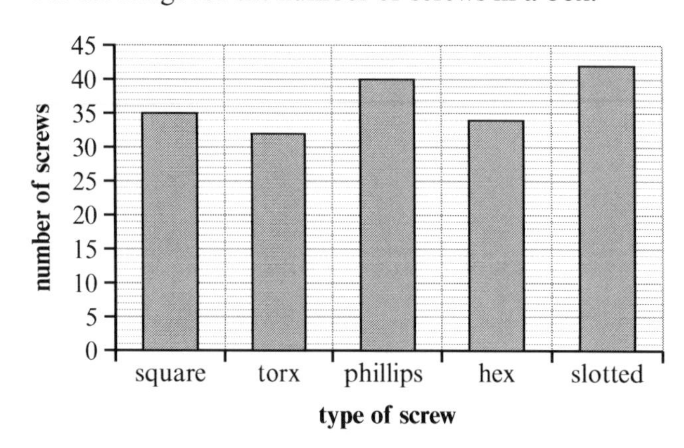

....

....

Making a decision

1 The company Sandeep works for runs a bonus scheme. For each car he sells, he receives a bonus payment. The value of the bonus payment depends on the value of the car he has sold.

Sandeep has to choose between Scheme A and Scheme B. He records the average number of cars per week that he sells in each price range and the bonus payment he would receive for them under each scheme in the table below.

Value of car	Average sales per week	Scheme A bonus (per car)	Scheme B bonus (per car)
up to £7,500	15	£75	£140
£7,500 to £15,000	21	£125	
over £15,000	9	£200	

Sandeep wants to earn as much as possible in bonus payments. Which scheme should he choose?

....

....

2 Mr and Mrs Brown are taking a group of children to the aquarium. They record the ages of the children in the table. Mr and Mrs Brown are both 46 years old.

The aquarium offers a group discount for children's parties. The discount is available to groups of 6 or more people with a median age of 12 or under. Can the group claim the discount? Explain your answer.

Name	Age (years)
Davydd	11
Katie	13
Aine	9
Rupert	11
Cedric	3

....

....

....

3 Two bus companies keep records of the number of buses that were late each month over a period of six months. This table shows the data that they collect.

	Jan	Feb	Mar	Apr	May	June
A2B Travels	24	28	29	25	28	18
Big Bus Com	20	19	25	23	29	21

A school wants to hire the company that has the lowest mean number of buses that are late. Which company should they choose?

....

....

....

Had a go ☐ Nearly there ☐ Nailed it! ☐

Likelihood

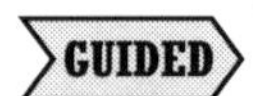

1 Draw line from each likelihood to each correct statement. One has been done for you.

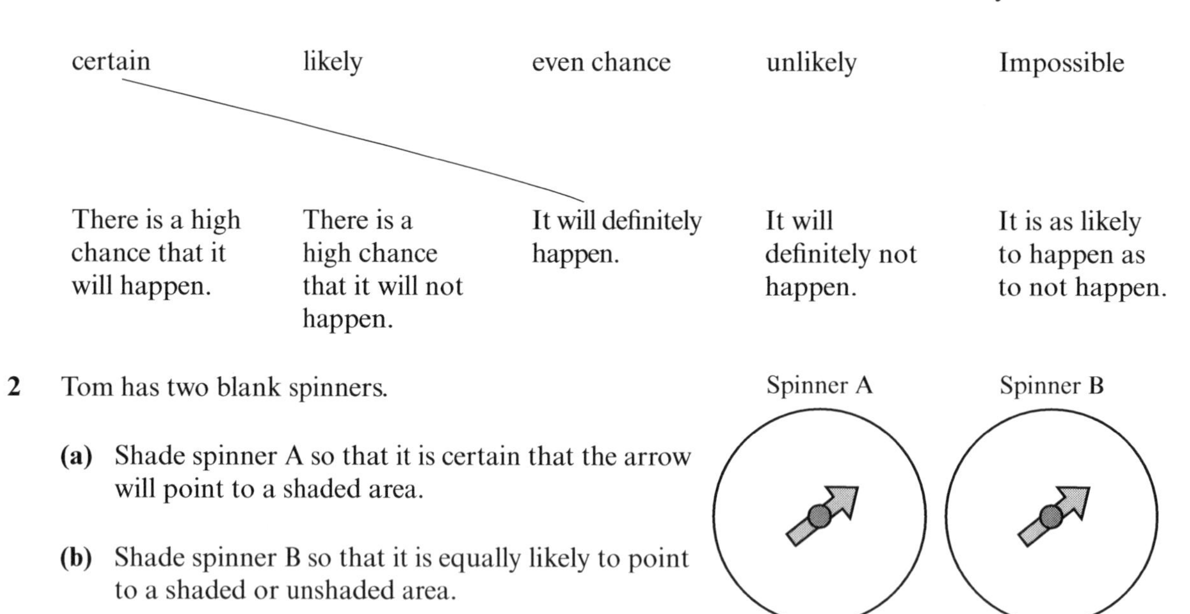

2 Tom has two blank spinners.

(a) Shade spinner A so that it is certain that the arrow will point to a shaded area.

(b) Shade spinner B so that it is equally likely to point to a shaded or unshaded area.

3 Sam keeps some white balls and black balls in different boxes. He is going to pick a white ball at random from the box. Complete the sentences using the boxes above.

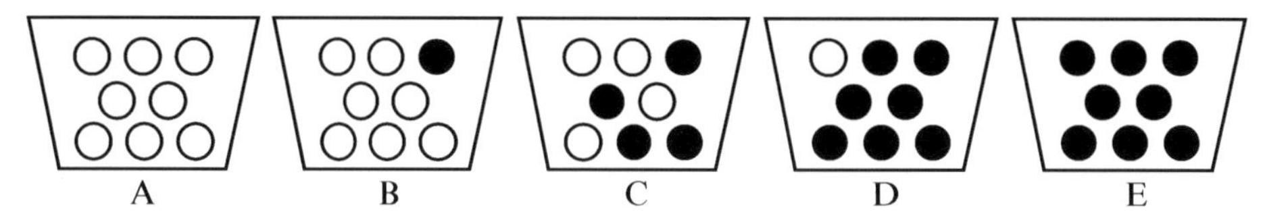

(a) It is impossible that Sam will pick a white ball from box ....

(b) It is likely that Sam will pick a white ball from box ....

(d) It is unlikely that Sam will pick a white ball from box ....

4 Cody is showing some cards to the pupils in her class.

She takes a card at random. One of her pupils says, 'I am less likely to choose a heart than a club.'

Is the pupil correct? Explain your answer.

....

....

....

Problem-solving practice

1 Matthew wants to do a charity walk and needs some equipment.

The table shows the prices of the items he needs from two different shops.

Item	Do Camping	Heptathlon	Quantity needed
water bottle	£6.50	£6.75	2
boots	£35.80	£32.99	1
coat	£47.00	£48.55	1
trousers	£26.95	£26.89	1
hat	£8.99	£7.95	2

Matthew has a budget of £140. He wants to buy all of the items in the same shop. Which shop should he buy his items from?

Work out the cost from each shop and then compare.

....

....

2 Cillian needs a data collection sheet to record information about people who want to join a computing department. The data he wants to record is:

- their name
- whether they have A levels or a degree
- whether they want to work in software or hardware.

Design a data collection sheet for Cillian to record this information.

3 PlumbWorld keeps a record of the length of time, in minutes, that their plumbers attend callouts. Here are the results for some of their plumbers..

39 48 45 64 83 42 61 54 59

(a) Work out:

(i) the mean ....

(ii) the range. ....

(b) Another company, FixIt, also kept a record of the length of time in minutes that their plumbers spent attending callouts. The mean length of time of a callout was 69 minutes and the range was 35 minutes.

Compare the callout times for each company.

....

....

Had a go ☐ Nearly there ☐ Nailed it! ☐

Problem-solving practice

1 Steven owns an ice cream parlour. The graph shows the number of ice creams sold each day during one week.

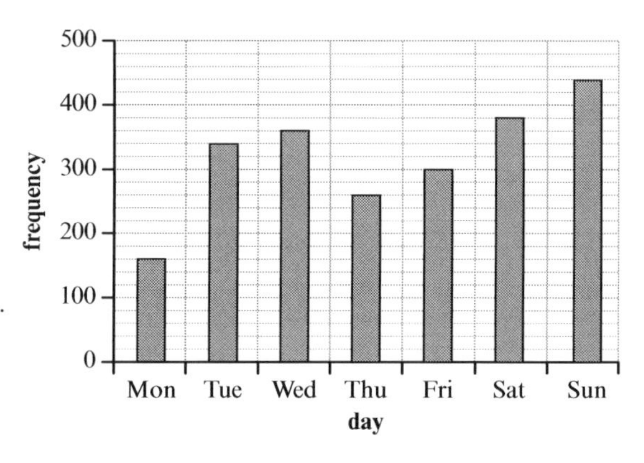

(a) How many ice creams were sold on Sunday?

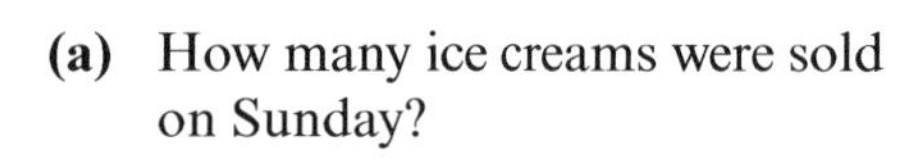

....

(b) How many more ice creams were sold in total from Monday to Friday than at the weekend?

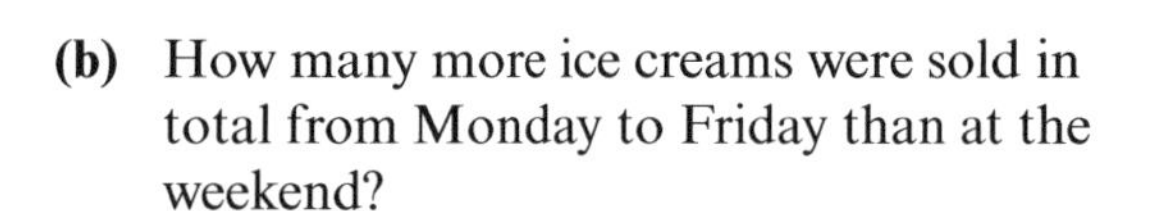

....

(c) Work out the mean number of ice creams sold per day.

....

(d) Work out the range of the number of ice creams sold each day during the week.

....

2 An events company asked two large supermarkets if their employees would be interested in participating in some activities. The activities are karting, paintball and climbing. The pie charts show the responses from the two supermarkets.

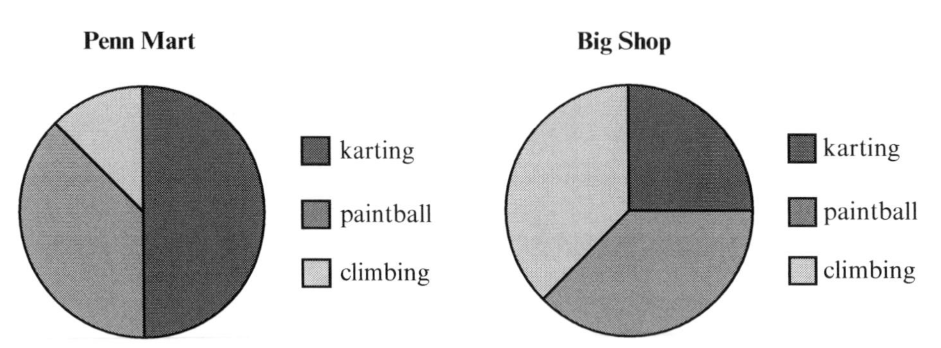

(a) 36 employees showed interest in Karting from Penn Mart.

How many people from Penn Mart took part in the survey?

....

(b) 20 employees showed interest in Karting from Big Shop.

How many people from Big Shop showed interest in paintball or climbing?

....

Problem-solving practice

1 This conversion graph can be used to change between kilometres per hour (km/h) and miles per hour (mph).

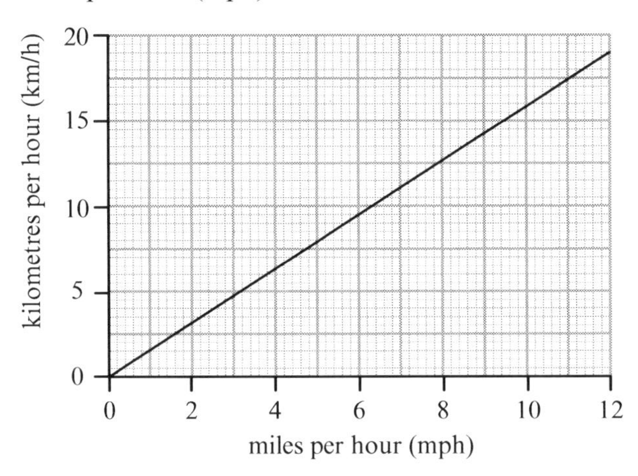

Sarah runs at an average speed of 6 mph and Ruth runs at an average speed of 11 km/h.

Who runs faster on average?

....

....

2 Tom works for a vending company. This table shows the information he collects about the number of drinks dispensed in five departments in a hospital over a period of a week.

Department	Paediatrics	A & E	Outpatient	Dermatology	ENT
Number of drinks	185	240	280	160	210

Draw a suitable graph or chart to show this information.

You should draw a bar chart for this data.

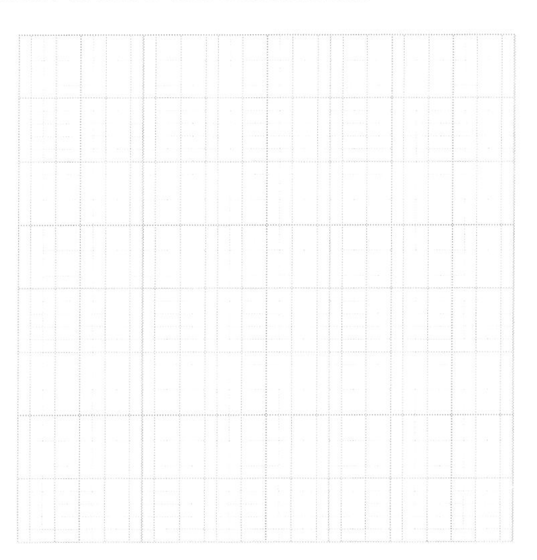

Practice paper

The practice test paper has been written to help you practise what you have learned and may not be representative of a real exam paper.

1 hour 30 minutes

The total mark for this paper is 48.

INSTRUCTIONS

- Use **black** ball-point pen.
- Answer **all** questions.
- Answer the questions in the spaces provided – there may be more space than you need.
- **Calculators may be used.**

INFORMATION

- The marks for each question are shown in brackets.
- **You must show clearly how you get your answers because marks will be awarded for your working out.**
- **Check your working and your answers at each stage.**

- **This sign shows where marks will be awarded for showing your check.**

SECTION A: Emily's Party

1 Emily is hosting a party for her friends.

She writes a list of the food she would like to buy. She works out that it will cost £45 in total.

Emily sees this offer:

Buy your groceries online and save 15% on your first order.

She works out that ordering her food online will save her £7.50

(a) Is she correct?

(2)

Use the box to show clearly how you get your answer.

Emily buys a leg of lamb for the party.

Emily uses this rule to work out how long to roast the lamb in minutes.

Weight of lamb (g)	→	Divide by 20	→	Add 25

Emily's leg of lamb weighs 2500 g.

(b) How long should Emily roast the lamb? Give your answer in minutes.

(3)

Use the box to show clearly how you get your answer.

Two shops sell party decorations.

Emily wants to buy a banner and some tea lights.

The shops have the following prices.

Shop 1	Shop 2
banner £4.75 each box of tea lights £2.85	banner £4.50 each box of tea lights £3.45 buy 2 boxes get 1 free

She wants to buy 1 banner and 3 boxes of tea lights.

(c) Which shop should Emily buy from?

(4)

Use the box to show clearly how you get your answer.

(Total for Question 1 is 9 marks)

2 Emily's friends are arriving at 18:30.

Emily plans to:

• go to the supermarket	50 minutes
• prepare the main meal	45 minutes
• feed the children	10 minutes
• shower	15 minutes
• get dressed and put on make up	30 minutes
• put the drinks out	15 minutes

Emily leaves the house for the supermarket at 15:50

Will Emily have enough time to complete all the tasks before 18:30?

(3)

Use the box to show clearly how you get your answer.

(Total for Question 2 is 3 marks)

3 Emily and her friends decide to take up running together. They want to work out how many calories they will use.

Emily checks in a running magazine and finds out that if she runs 250 m, she will use 22 calories.

She suggests running 2 km a week.

Emily works out that she will use 180 calories on each run.

Is Emily correct?

(4)

Use the box to show clearly how you get your answer.

(Total for Question 3 is 4 marks)

SECTION B: Taxi Services

4 Ravina works for an accounts company.

She is auditing the accounts for two taxi firms.

The taxi firms are called ABC and GoGo.

She draws the following graphs to show the monthly income figures for ABC and GoGo.

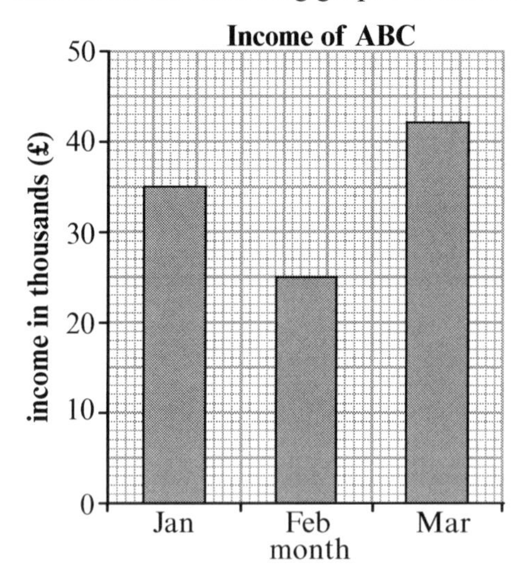

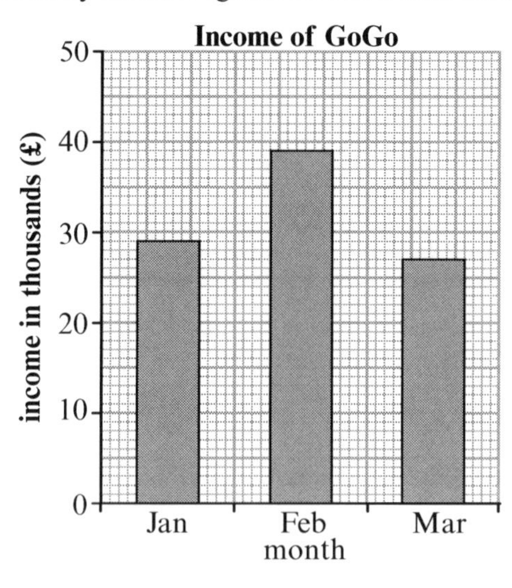

Ravina thinks that the total income figures for ABC are less than the total income figures for GoGo for these 3 months.

Is she correct?

(5)

Use the box to show clearly how you get your answer.

(Total for Question 4 is 5 marks)

5 Anjali is a driver for another taxi firm called SuperDrop.

Anjali needs to take a customer to the airport.

The customer needs to arrive by 10 p.m. to check in on time.

The airport is 150 miles away from where Anjali collects the customer.

Anjali can drive at 60 mph.

She starts the journey at 7.15 p.m.

(a) Will they arrive at the airport for the customer to check in?

(3)

Use the box to show clearly how you get your answer.

One of the cars at SuperDrop needs some repairs.

The taxi firm decide to hire another car while the other taxi is getting repaired.

Stephen finds a hire company and they send him an email with the following information.

Car hire rates	
£75 plus:	
Mon–Thurs	£30 per day
Fri–Sun	£63 per day

The car will be hired from Tuesday 18 September till Thursday 27 September.

(b) How much will it cost the taxi firm to hire the car?

(4)

Use the box to show clearly how you get your answer.

(Total for Question 5 is 7 marks)

6 The owner of the taxi firm wants to move into a new office.

He asks Matthew to plan the new office.

Matthew draws a plan of the office on centimetre-squared paper.

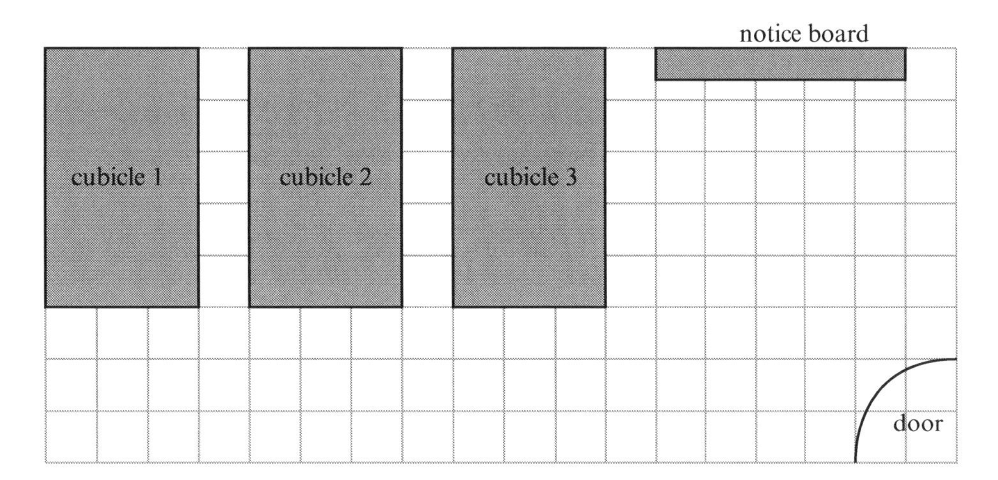

Key: 1 cm on the grid represents 50 cm in the office

Matthew wants to have space for a cabinet and a washroom.

The space for the cabinet must be rectangular, 100 cm long by 50 cm wide. It must be against a wall, but not in front of the notice board.

The space for the washroom must be rectangular, 200 cm long and 100 cm wide in a corner.

Show on the plan where he could place the cabinet and the washroom.

(4)

(Total for Question 6 is 4 marks)

SECTION C: Work Pays

7 Mahad is working as a salesperson for Celestricity selling solar panels.

His target earnings for this week are £335

This table shows his earnings for Monday, Tuesday, Wednesday and Thursday.

Day	Amount earned (£)
Monday	57.60
Tuesday	64.80
Wednesday	36.00
Thursday	93.60

Mahad needs to work on Friday to meet his target of £335

He plans to work 12 hours. He is paid £7.20 per hour.

He thinks he will meet his target.

(a) Is Mahad correct?

Show a check of your working.

(5)

Use the box to show clearly how you get your answer.

Show your check in the box below.

☑

Mahad wants to know his average weekly wage.

This table shows information about his weekly wages for the last 6 weeks.

Week	Wage (£)
1	421
2	235
3	380
4	340
5	276
6	310

(b) What is his mean weekly wage?

(2)

Use the box to show clearly how you get your answer.

(Total for Question 7 is 7 marks)

8 The human resources manager wants to introduce a company car scheme.

She needs to provide the different choices the salespeople can have.

The salespeople can have:

- petrol or diesel
- a small car or an executive car
- lease or hire purchase

The human resources manager wants to put the choices of each salesperson on one sheet.

There are 6 salespeople.

Design a data collection sheet for the manager to use.

(3)

Use the space below to draw your answer.

(Total for Question 8 is 3 marks)

9 Celestricity is offering a training course for its employees.

They need to provide transport for their employees.

The table shows information about the number of minibuses available and the number of seats on each minibus.

Minibus	Number of seats	Number of minibuses available
large	15	4
small	9	8

There are 96 employees.

(a) How many of each type of minibus should Celestricity use?

(3)

Use the box to show clearly how you get your answer.

The training course tutors decide to plan lunch at a restaurant.

There are 8 tutors. The cost of lunch for 8 people at the restaurant is £340, excluding the service charge.

There is a service charge of £3 for each tutor.

The cost of the lunch is divided amongst the 8 tutors.

The waiter calculates that each tutor should pay £44.50

(b) Is the waiter correct?

(3)

Use the box to show clearly how you get your answer.

(Total for Question 9 is 6 marks)

ANSWERS

INTRODUCTION

1. Online test preparation

1

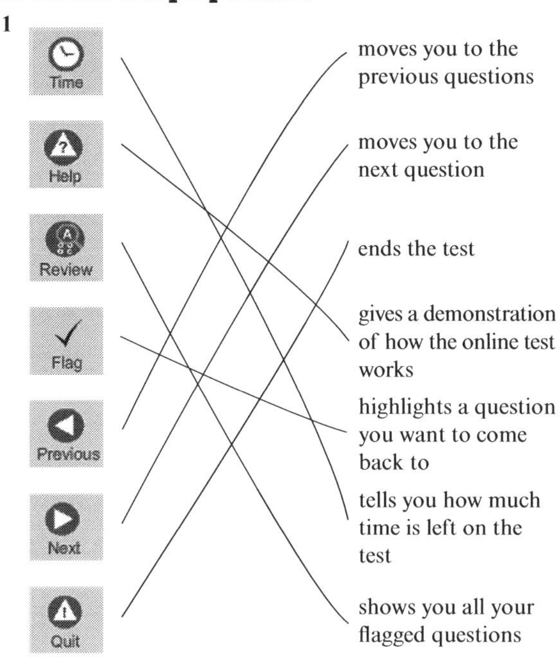

2 **(a)** scrolls across or up and down the screen
(b) zooms in or out
(c) returns to the default colours
(d) returns the screen to the default size
(e) lets you change colours.

3 **(a)** 15, 5 **(b)** timer **(c)** settings, colour, zoom

2. Online test tools

1 **(a)** working out space **(b)** calculator

2 drag and drop

3 Click and drag the square onto the grid. Click and drag the corners to adjust the size.

4 Click on the points and drag up or down.

3. Using the onscreen calculator

1 **(a)** 1024 **(b)** 35

2 £1.30

3 $(35 \times 8 \times 5) \div 25 = 56$

4 $28 \times 7.49 + 4 \times 13.99 =$ £265.68

5 $325 \times 1.35 + 48 \times 4.85 =$ £671.55

NUMBER

4. Number and place value

1. **(a)** Forty-five thousand, six hundred and seventy-two
(b) Seven hundred and forty-three thousand, five hundred and eight

2 **(a)** 406 353 **(b)** 5 734 901

3 **(a)** 40 **(b)** 4000 **(c)** 4

4 parcel A

5 £278,499, £289,905, £289,995, £326,500, £326,550

5. Negative numbers

1 **(a)** −9 and −2
(b) −53 and −12

2 −13, −7, −2, −1, 7

3 4 °C, −1 °C , −2 °C, −10 °C

4 **(a)** hydrogen **(b)** mercury

5 March, June, April, May, January, February

6. Rounding

1 **(a)** 40 **(b)** 2790

2 **(a)** 100 **(b)** 5900 **(c)** 57 200

3 **(a)** 6000 **(b)** 43 000 **(c)** 623 000

4 **(a)** 20 **(b)** 2700 **(c)** 15 000

5 No, he should have written 240 not 24

7. Adding and subtracting

1 £146

2 42

3 £858

4 No, it should have been £229

5 £166

8. Multiplying and dividing by 10, 100 and 1000

1 **(a)** 90 **(b)** 7

2 12 mm

3 They should book with Top Choice, as £2,200 is less than £2,220

4 £2,060

9. Multiplication and division

1 768 flowers

2 **(a)** 6 boxes **(b)** 14 boxes

3 £975

4 17

5 £527

10. Squares and multiples

1 $1^2 = 1$, $2^2 = 4$, $3^2 = 9$, $4^2 = 16$, $5^2 = 25$, $6^2 = 36$, $7^2 = 49$, $8^2 = 64$, $9^2 = 81$, $10^2 = 100$

2 **(a)** 8 16 24 32 40 48 56 64 72 80
(b) 17 34 51 68 85 102 119 136 153 170
(c) 28 56 84 112 140 168 196 224 252 280

3 **(a)** 20 **(b)** 25

4 **(a)** 18 **(b)** 60 **(c)** 84

5 8 packs of sausages and 15 packs of buns

11. Estimating

You might work out your estimates differently but make sure they are sensible.

1 **(a)** 140 **(b)** 860 **(c)** 10 800 **(d)** 8

2 **(a)** £15,000 **(b)** £20,400

3 £60,000

4 8

5 £24,000

6 **(a)** 1700 g **(b)** 100 coins

7 150 000 bolts

12. Checking your answer

1 **(b)** 340 so 379 is likely to be correct
(c) 900 so 932 is likely to be correct

2 **(a)** correct **(b)** correct
(c) incorrect **(d)** incorrect

3 $80 \times 30 \div 40 = 60$ so she is likely to be correct.

4 $800 - 80 - 200 =$ £520 so he is likely to have enough money to pay for the holiday.

13. Word problems

1 Finance deal = £15,100 so the cash price is cheaper

2 **(a)** £157 **(b)** No, she will only raise $26 \times$ £6 = £156

3 Yes as the cost of tickets is £257

14. Fractions

1 **(a)** shaded $= \frac{3}{16}$ not shaded $= \frac{13}{16}$
(b) shaded $= \frac{5}{24}$ not shaded $= \frac{19}{24}$

2 **(a)** $\frac{6}{15}$ **(b)** $\frac{4}{15}$ **(c)** $\frac{5}{15}$

3 $\frac{1}{2}$ kg

5

	Square	Round	Total
Dark	27	13	40
Milk	23	17	40
Total	50	30	80

15. Equivalent fractions

1 **(a)** $\frac{18}{24}$ or $\frac{3}{4}$
(b)

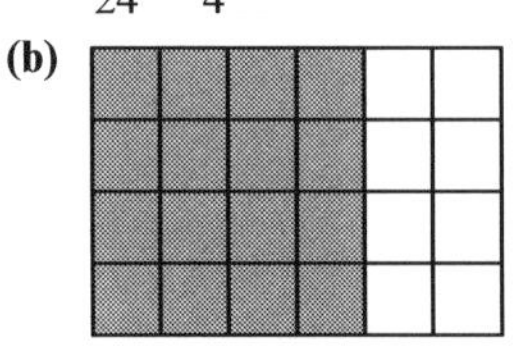

2 The smaller fraction is $\frac{3}{4}$

3 $\frac{2}{3}$

4 Bill ate more.

5 $\frac{1}{2}, \frac{3}{5}, \frac{3}{4}$

16. Mixed numbers

1 **(a)** $\frac{16}{5}$ **(b)** $\frac{7}{3}$ **(c)** $\frac{36}{7}$

2 **(a)** $5\frac{1}{2}$ **(b)** $2\frac{1}{5}$ **(c)** $10\frac{1}{4}$

3 $\frac{34}{3}$ — $11\frac{1}{3}$
$\frac{26}{5}$ — $5\frac{1}{5}$
$\frac{79}{8}$ — $9\frac{7}{8}$
$\frac{92}{11}$ — $8\frac{4}{11}$

4 **(a)** $3\frac{1}{4}$ **(b)** $\frac{6}{5}$

5 She is not correct. $1\frac{1}{8} = \frac{9}{8}$ which is not the same as $\frac{11}{9}$

17. Fractions of amounts

1 **(a)** 45 **(b)** 60 **(c)** 64

2 **(a)** 117 **(b)** 78

3 **(a)** 50 000 **(b)** 100 000 **(c)** 25 000

4 Amy

5 £190

18. Word problems with fractions

1 15

2 Sport4life, because the price is £39 rather than £42 at Trainers Ltd

3 Cheap Posts, because it will cost £100, against £105 from Fence World

4 She should use her railcard.

19. Decimals

1 **(a)** 8 tenths **(b)** 9 hundredths
(c) 3 thousandths

2 1.4, 3.2, 6.2, 6.4, 12.8

3 £15.04, £15.05, £15.40, £15.50

4 0.06, 0.7, 0.71, 0.711, 0.713

5 10.779, 10.8, 10.825, 10.83, 10.88

6 **(a)** 12.8 **(b)** 15.94 **(c)** 9.04

20. Decimal calculations

1 5.47 cm

2 0.8 miles

3 70.61 seconds

4 £2.75

5 He is wrong. It costs £1.99

21. Rounding decimals and estimating

1 **(a)** 4 **(b)** 5 **(c)** 11

2 **(a)** 5 m **(b)** 10 cm **(c)** 79 ml

3 108 square feet

4 Kaine spent more

22. Word problems with decimals

1 £1,203

2 He has enough money as the total is £88.10

3 Sales assistant

4 40.25 litres

23. Fractions and decimals

1 **(a)** 0.3 **(b)** 0.16 **(c)** 0.35 **(d)** 0.625

2 **(a)** $\frac{1}{3}$ **(b)** $\frac{4}{7}$

3 **(a)** $\frac{3}{4}$ **(b)** $\frac{5}{9}$

4

Weight (kg)	$5\frac{1}{2}$	$5\frac{2}{3}$	$5\frac{7}{8}$	$5\frac{1}{4}$	$5\frac{4}{9}$
Order	3	4	5	1	2

5 **(a)** 00450, 01045, 01450, 01549, 02033
(b) $7\frac{5}{16}, 7\frac{3}{8}, 7\frac{3}{5}, 8\frac{1}{6}, 8\frac{1}{3}$

24. Percentages

1 **(a)** 48% **(b)** 98%

2 7%

3 4%

4 College A, because the same number of people passed at each college but fewer people took the test at College A, so the percentage of people who passed must be greater.

5 39%

25. Calculating percentage parts

1 **(a)** 5.5 **(b)** 15.75

2 **(a)** £5.88 **(b)** £103.88

3 £75,880

4 Gaming World

26. Fractions, decimals and percentages

1 **(a)** $\frac{7}{10}$, 71%, 0.73 **(b)** $\frac{9}{25}$, 0.4, 42%

2 £1,496

3 30

4 £50.50

5 £900

27. Word problems with percentages

1 Bikeys

2 £18,126

3 £5,000

4 £2,158.50

28. Using formulas

1 104 minutes

2 £269

3 £170

4 56 920

29. Ratio

1

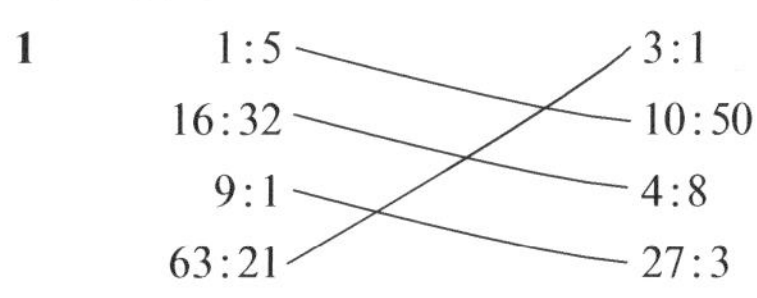

2 **(a)** 1:2 **(b)** 1:5 **(c)** 1:2 **(d)** 1:8

3 **(a)**

Amount of pineapple squash	Amount of water
5	30
1	6
8	48
12	72

(b) 1:6

4 5:1

5 Yes, they are both in the ratio 1:3

30. Ratio problems

1 **(a)** 1:8 **(b)** 1:12 **(c)** 5:1 **(d)** 1:10

2 **(a)** 1:7 **(b)** 1:14

3 £198

4 54

5 **(a)** 1350 ml **(b)** 180 ml and 1620 ml

31. Proportion

1 £86.68

2 £97.80

3 56 glasses

4 Large

5 **(a)** 125 ml **(b)** No she is not correct. She will need 1500 ml of fertiliser.

6 Offer 2

32. Recipes

1 800 g sugar, 16 g butter, 640 g condensed milk and 120 ml milk

2 900 g flour, 150 g currants, 9 eggs and 450 ml milk

3 He does not have enough ingredients (he needs 360 g flour).

33. Word problems with ratio

1 1:3

2 No as 6 adults can only take 54 children

3 £2,604

4 Yes, Paul is right as he will use 1680 g in 4 weeks.

5 £74.25

34. Problem-solving practice

1 35%

2 **(a)** £15.56 **(b)** 7 **(c)** £1.78

3 **(a)** £111.92 **(b)** £153

35. Problem-solving practice

1 **(a)** 5 packs of holders

(b) £4.60

2 **(a)** Yes, the ratio is 20:100

(b) Yes, he burns 986 calories.

36. Problem-solving practice

1 No, as £105 is less than £126

2 £9.70

3 £333.75

4 Brett should not get a water meter.

TIME

37. Units of time

1 **(a)** 240 **(b)** 3600

2 **(a)** 15 **(b)** 1440

3 **(a)** 72 **(b)** 168

4 **(a)** 70 **(b)** 500

5 2 hours 20 minutes

6 4 hours 5 minutes

7 4 hours 20 minutes

38. Dates

1 **(a)** Saturday 7 May

(b) Monday 16 May

(c) Friday 20 May

2 **(a)** 9 **(b)** 19 **(c)** 25

3 **(a)** 28 **(b)** Monday 6 November

39. 12-hour and 24-hour clocks

1 **(a)** 10:30 **(b)** 14:25 **(c)** 16:28
(d) 05:15 **(e)** 00:05 **(f)** 12:15

2 **(a)** 8.32 a.m. **(b)** 3.16 p.m. **(c)** 8.35 p.m.
(d) 6.42 p.m. **(e)** 11.45 a.m. **(f)** 4.30 p.m.

3 1 hour 54 minutes

4 **(a)** 13:30 **(b)** 16:05

5 **(a)** 10:25 11:05 11:45
(b) 10:10 10:50 11:30 12:10
(c) He started 12:05 and finished at 12:30

40. Timetables

1 **(a)** 06:21 **(b)** 51 minutes

2 **(a)** 11 hours 57 minutes **(b)** at the weekend

3 **(a)** 08:45 **(b)** 1 hour 32 minutes **(c)** 08:15

41. Creating a time plan

1

shorten trousers	8.00 a.m. – 9.10 a.m
shortening skirt	9.10 a.m. – 9.55 a.m.
tea break	9.55 a.m. – 10.15 a.m.
shortening sleeves	10.15 a.m. – 11.30 a.m.
lunch	11.30 a.m. – 12.30 p.m.
reline jacket	12.30 p.m. – 3.00 p.m.

2

08:00 – 08:30	meet Mr Smith
08:30 – 09:00	meet Mrs Ahmad
10:00 – 10:50	car demo
11:00 – 13:15	training
13:15 – 14:15	complete paperwork
15:00 – 15:50	car demo
16:00	finish

3 No, she will run over by 45 minutes.

42. Problem-solving practice

1 18:30

2 10 hours

3

11:00	C v. H
11:40	break
11:55	P v. W
12:35	break
12:50	C v. P
13:30	break
13:45	H v. W
14:25	break
14:40	H v. P
15:20	break
15:35	C v. W
16:15	end

4 **(a)** 15 November **(b)** 29 December

43. Problem-solving practice

1 17 March

2 **(a)** 22 minutes **(b)** 14:02
(c) 2 hours 48 minutes **(d)** 15:56

3 **(a)** 18 hours 15 minutes
(b) An example time plan:

09:00	start
09:15–10:00	finger printing
10:45–12:00	advanced driving
12:15–12:45	diversity
13:00–13:30	compulsory

MEASURES

44. Units

1

Weight	Distance	Capacity
kilograms grams tonnes	kilometre millimetre centimetre	litres millilitres centilitres

2 **(a)** kilograms **(b)** kilometres
(c) metres **(d)** centimetres

3 **(a)** 1.6 m **(b)** 5–10 g **(c)** 330 ml

4 No. If the man is just under 2 m tall, the truck is about 4 m tall which is taller than the bridge.

45. Measuring lines

1 **(a)** 4 cm
(b) 3.5 cm
(c) 1.8 cm

2 Measure your lines carefully to check they are the correct length.

3 Check your cross is at 4.2 cm.

4 17.2 cm

46. Scales

1 **(a)** 24 **(b)** 320 **(c)** 4900 **(d)** 4.3

2 **(a)** 200 300 400

(b) 3 4 5

3 160 ml

4 **(a)** 65 km/h
(b)

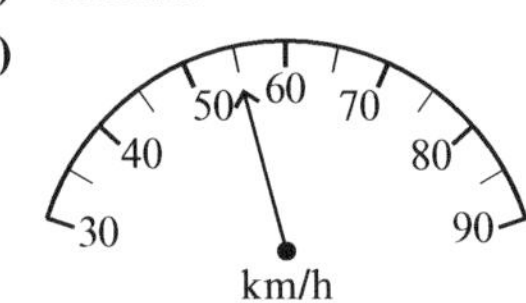

47. Mileage charts

1 **(a)** 206 miles **(b)** **(i)** Cambridge **(ii)** Exeter

2 **(a)** 48 miles **(b)** 120 miles

3 **(a)** 260 miles **(b)** 172

48. Routes

1 2485 metres

2 9:22

3 office to Baggeridge to Conway to Ashton to office. Length of journey is 42.6 miles

49. Length

1

mm ⟶ cm	÷ 10	cm ⟶ mm	× 10
cm ⟶ m	÷ 100	m ⟶ cm	× 100
m ⟶ km	÷ 1000	km ⟶ m	× 1000

2 **(a)** 3.5 cm **(b)** 830 mm **(c)** 4600 m **(d)** 3.9 km

3 80 cm, 8000 mm, 80 m

4 **(a)** 21 200 mm **(b)** 3 202 205 mm

5 14

6 Yes, she will.

50. Weight

1

kg ⟶ g	× 1000	g ⟶ kg	÷ 1000
g ⟶ mg	× 1000	mg ⟶ g	÷ 1000

2 **(a)** 6200 g **(b)** 5.8 kg **(c)** 0.64 g
(d) 0.586 kg

3 400 000 mg 4 kg 40 000 g

4 **(a)** 3254.5 g **(b)** 10 187 g

5 20

6 No. 4950 g is less than 5000 g.

51. Capacity

1

litres ⟶ centilitres	× 100	centilitres ⟶ litres	÷ 100
centilitres ⟶ millilitres	× 10	millilitres ⟶ centilitres	÷ 10
litres ⟶ millilitres	× 1000	millilitres ⟶ litres	÷ 1000

2 **(a)** 830 cl **(b)** 7600 ml **(c)** 0.64 litres **(d)** 7.8 litres

3 6 litres 6300 cl 63 500 ml

4 **(a)** 1220.9 cl **(b)** 1210 cl

5 60

6 13 minutes 20 seconds

52. Money

1 **(a)** 38p **(b)** 15 289p

2 **(a)** £9.67 **(b)** £782.16

3 **(a)** £8.22 **(b)** £6.68

4 £1.75

5 £159.18

6 Gary's groceries

53. Temperature

1 **(a)** 10 °C **(b)** −7 °C

2 **(a)**

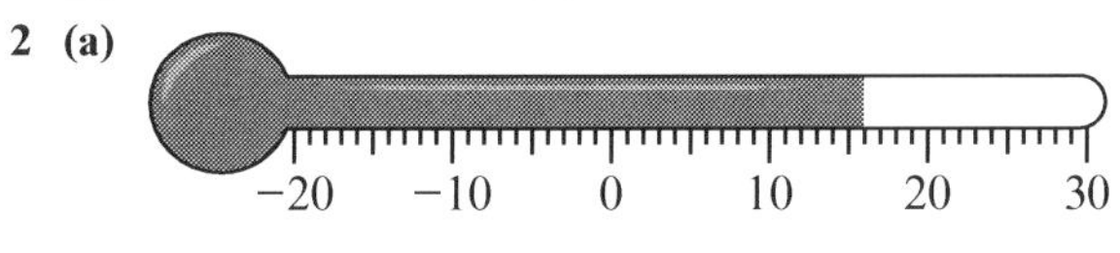

(b)

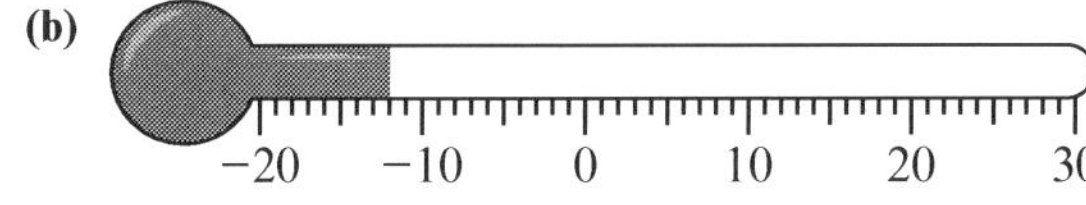

3 **(a)** 7 °C **(b)** 22 degrees **(c)** −3 °C

4 **(a)** −2 °C **(b)** −8 °C **(c)** −15 °C
(d) 23 degrees

54. Perimeter and area

1 **(a)** area = 6 cm^2, perimeter = 12 cm
(b) area = 8 cm^2, perimeter = 14 cm

2 **(a)** 6 cm^2 **(b)** 9 cm^2

3 **(a)** 38 cm **(b)** 37 cm

55. Area of rectangles

1 **(a)** 84 cm^2 **(b)** 24 m^2

2 **(a)** 8 cm **(b)** 17 m

3 24 sheep

4 She does not have enough. She needs £600

56. Problem-solving practice

1 £3.59

2 **(a)** 1.8 m **(b)** 5.4 m

3 9 pack is the better value for money.

4 150 g

57. Problem-solving practice

1

Bangor				
54	Llangollen			
152	98	Nuneaton		
67	13	85	Oswestry	
136	82	16	69	Tamworth

2 Alton to Boswell to Carlton to Denton to Alton, 128 kilometres

58. Problem-solving practice

1 £157.50

2 48 tiles

3 Yes, as £132.75 is less than £180

SHAPE AND SPACE

59. Symmetry

1 **(a)**

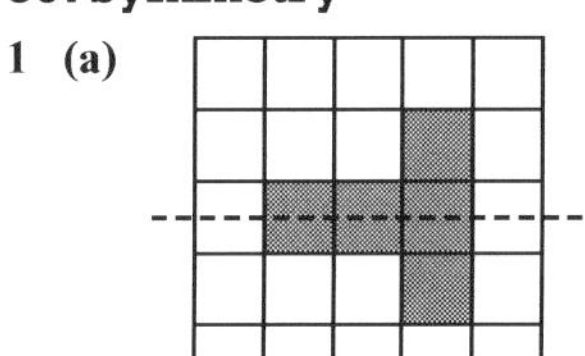

(b)

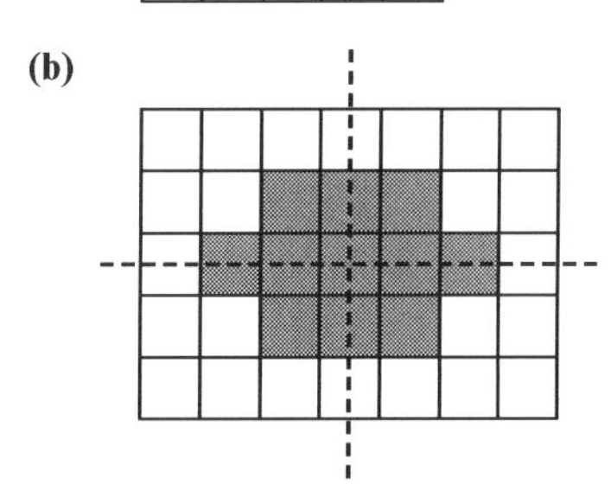

2 **(a)** A **(b)** B or C **(c)** D

3 **(a)**

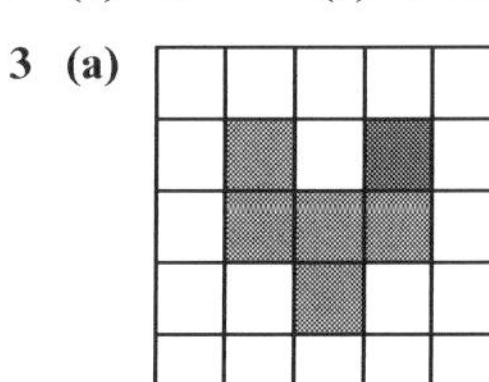

(b)

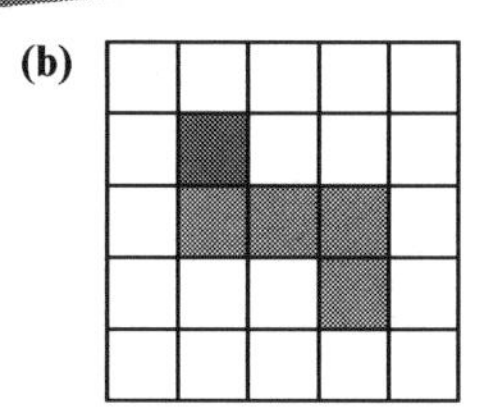

(c)

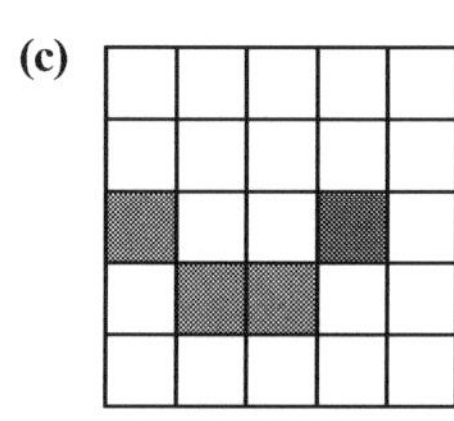

(d)

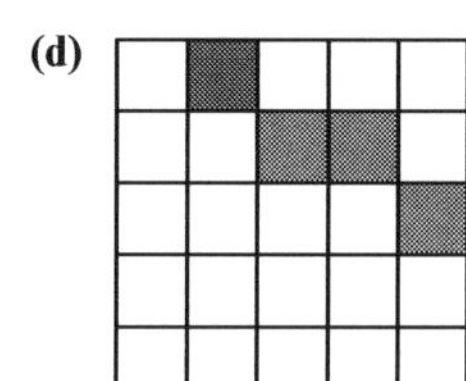

60. Properties of 2D shapes

1

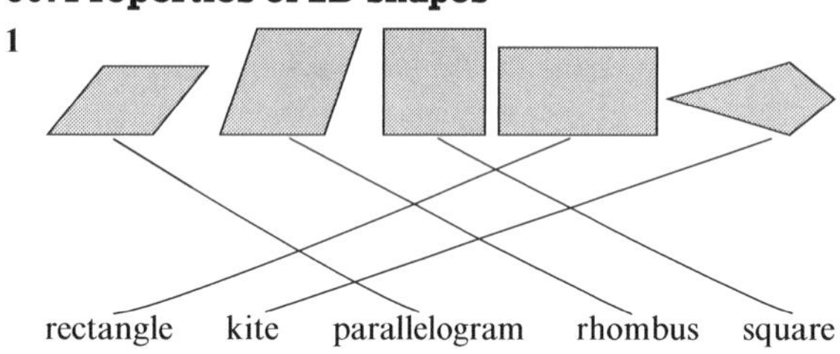

2

Name of shape	Regular	Irregular
triangle		
hexagon		
quadrilateral		
octagon		

3 **(a)** 216 **(b)** No, she needs £330

61. Scale drawings and maps

1 **(a)** 15 m **(b)** 200 km

2 188 km

3 5 km

4 150 cm

5 512

62. Using plans

1 There are many possible solutions. For example:

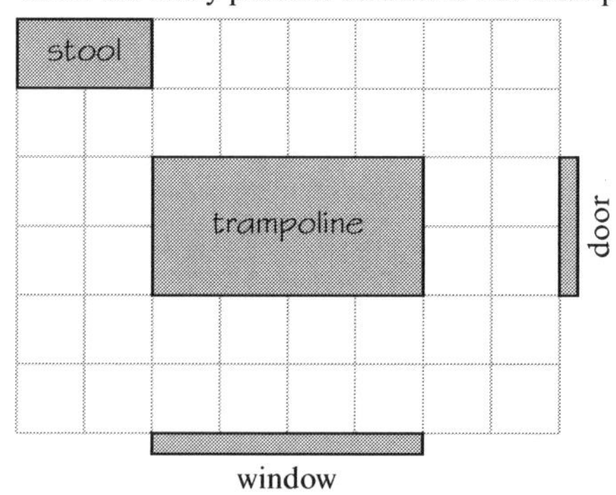

2 There are many possible solutions. For example:

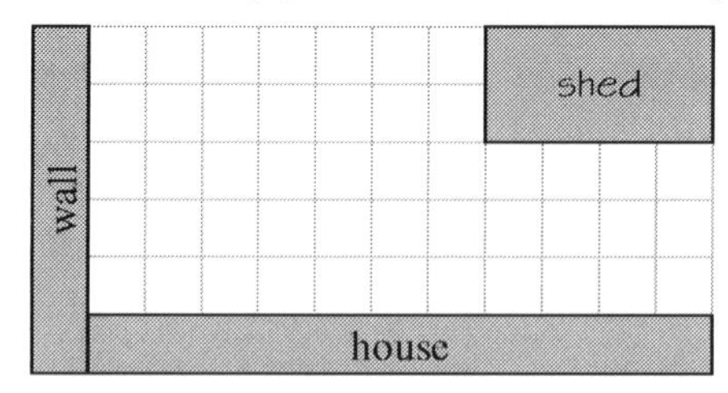

3 There are many possible solutions. For example:

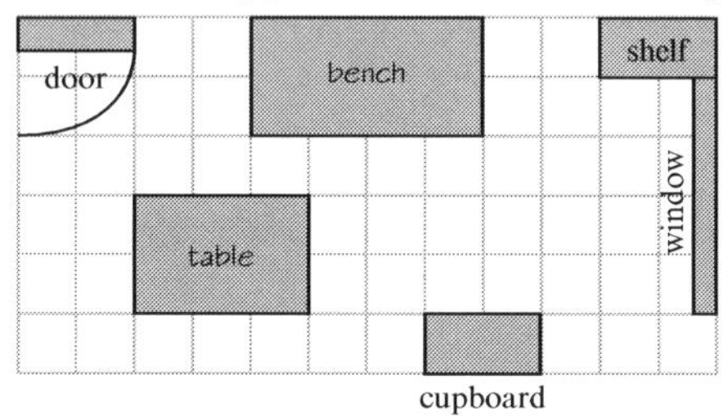

63. Angles

1

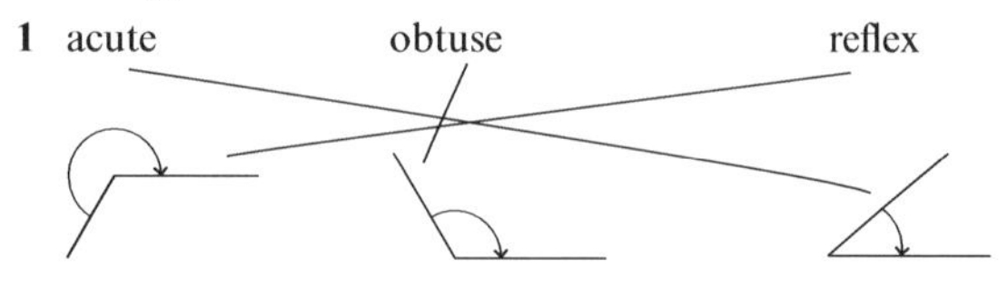

2 **(a)** Obtuse because it is between 90° and 180°.

(b) Reflex because it is more than 180°.

3 **(a)** about 30° **(b)** about 45°

4 **(a)** $p = 32°$, $q = 133°$ and $r = 15°$

(b) $e = 68°$, $f = 101°$, $g = 115°$ and $h = 76°$

64. Problem-solving practice

1 175 miles

2 Chrissie would need to buy 6 packs from Handyware Mansion for £270 in total or 14 packs from Do It Yourself Hypermarket for £266 in total. This means she should buy ceiling tiles from Do It Yourself Hypermarket.

3 **(a)** 1.35 m **(b)** 33 cm

65. Problem-solving practice

1 vinyl floor tiles (8 packs)

2

radiator | door | bed | rug | window | cupboard

HANDLING DATA

66. Tables

1 **(a)** £2.90 **(b)** £41.80 **(c)** £11.50

2 Yes, he earns £1,028.60

3 £1,105.82 from Wackes

67. Tally charts and frequency tables

1 **(a)**

Animal	cow	hen	pig	sheep
Tally	𝍸 𝍸 𝍸 |||	𝍸 𝍸 ||||	𝍸 𝍸		𝍸 |||
Frequency	18	14	11	8

(b) 14 **(c)** 51

2 **(a)**

Method of travel	bike	bus	car	walk
Tally	|||	𝍸 𝍸 ||	𝍸		𝍸 ||||
Frequency	3	12	6	9

(b) bus

(c) 6

3

Type of vehicle	car	coach	motorhome	lorry
Frequency	52	26	12	12

68. Data collection sheets

1 **(a)**

Colour	black	blue	red	white
Tally	|||	||||	𝍸		𝍸 ||
Frequency	3	4	6	7

(b) white

(c) 20

2 **(a)**

	Mon	**Tues**	**Weds**
Books borrowed			
Opening hours			

(b) 68

3

Table	
Soup	
Pate	
Curry	
Lasagne	
Ice cream	
Cheesecake	

69. Reading bar charts

1 Any two from: label missing on one bar, no label on vertical axis, vertical scale is not correct

2 **(a)** 16 **(b)** 4 **(c)** 44

3 **(a)** 25 **(b)** Thursday **(c)** 20 **(d)** 160

70. Reading pictograms

1 **(a)** 40 **(b)** Wednesday

2 **(a)** chocolate **(b)** 10

3. **(a)** 10 **(b)** 104

71. Reading pie charts

1 **(a)** salmon **(b)** $\frac{1}{4}$ **(c)** 112

2 **(a)** blue **(b)** 60 **(c)** You cannot tell because you do not know how many the total numbers of children there are in Woodfield School.

3 Taran won more by 3 games.

72. Reading line graphs

1 Lorry A has more diesel.

2 Pam's bag weighs less.

3 **(a)** 3 degrees **(b)** It decreases.

73. Planning a graph or chart

1 **(a)** month

(b) temperature (°C)

(c) Go up in multiples of 2

(d) bar chart or line graph

2 **(a)** week

(b) profit (£)

(c) Go up in multiples of 1000

(d) bar chart or line graph

3 **(a)** day

(b) number of cars

(c) Go up in multiples of 2

(d) bar chart

74. Drawing bar charts

1

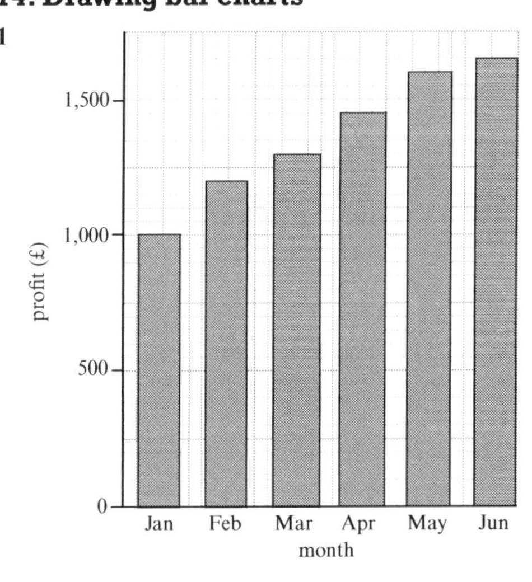

2

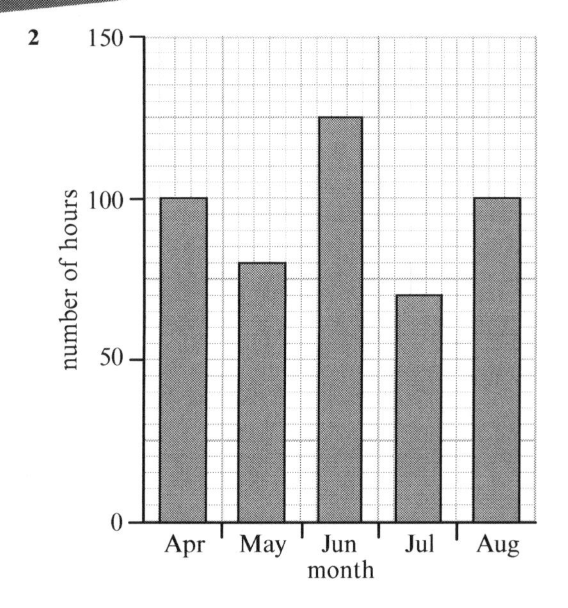

75. Drawing pictograms

1 **(a)** 6 **(b)** 3

(c)

Monday	
Tuesday	
Wednesday	
Thursday	
Friday	

Key: represents 2 hours

2 **(a)** 8 **(b)** 38

(c)

Monday	
Tuesday	
Wednesday	
Thursday	
Friday	

76. Drawing line graphs

1

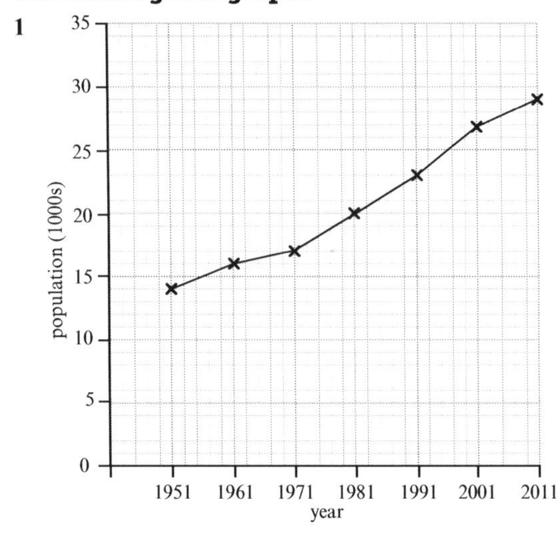

2

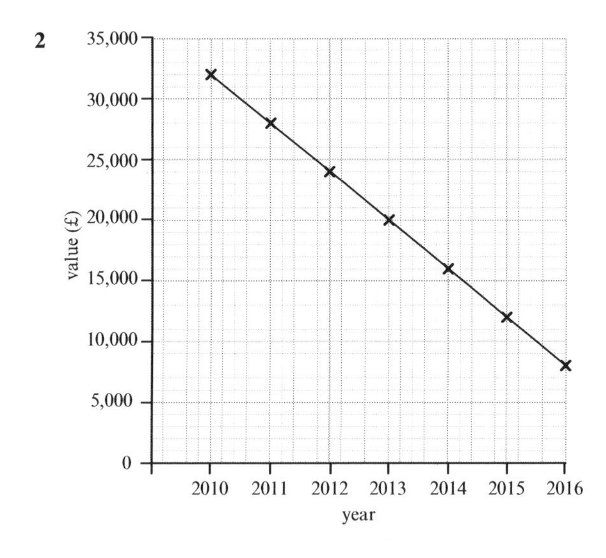

77. Mean

1 5

2 total = £58,760, mean = £7,345 so Roy will give the plumbers a pay rise.

3 total = 2555, mean = £365 so no, they cannot as 365 is less than 375.

4 No, the mean is 106.33p, which is more than 105.7p

78. Range

1 13

2 The range of carpentry marks is 6 and the range of retail marks is 5 so the tutor is correct.

3 8

4 10

79. Making a decision

1 scheme A = £5,550
scheme B = £6,300
He should choose scheme B (£6,300) as it is greater than scheme A (£5,550)

2 Yes because there are 7 people in the group and the median age is 11

3 A2B = 25.3 Big Bus Com = 22.8
They should choose Big Bus Com as it is less late on average.

80. Likelihood

1

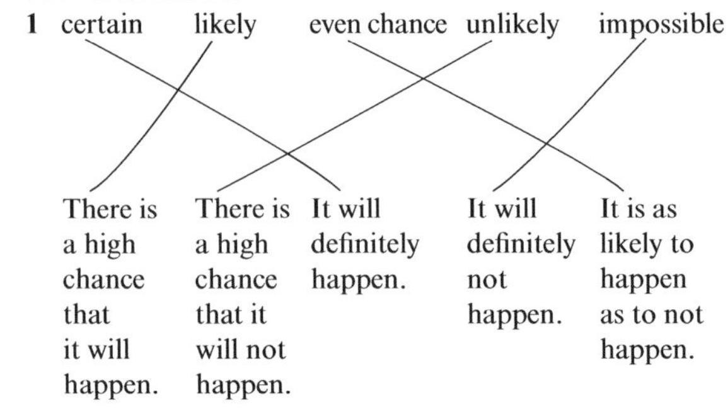

2 (a)

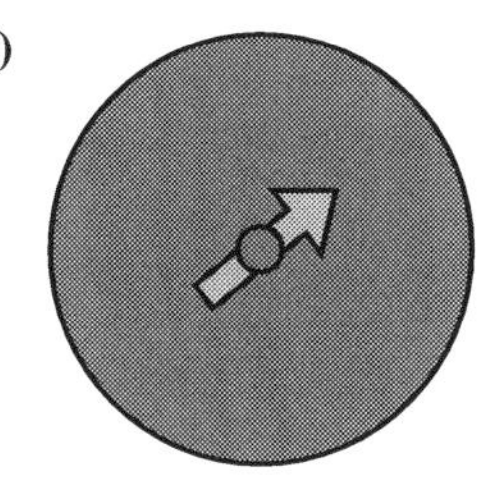

(b)

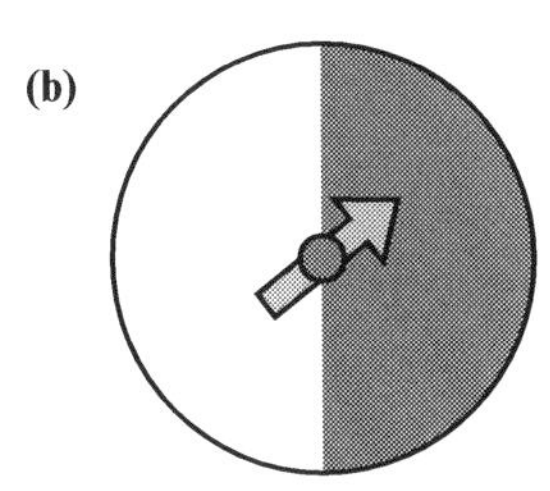

3 **(a)** E **(b)** B **(c)** D

4 No, as there are equal numbers of hearts and clubs.

81. Problem-solving practice

1 Heptathlon

2

Name	A level	Degree	Software	Hardware
Anton				
Dylan				
Frank				
Wayne				

3 **(a)** **(i)** 55 **(ii)** 44

(b) On average the callouts for FixIt lasted longer. The range was larger for PlumbWorld, meaning that the length of their callouts were more spread out.

82. Problem-solving practice

1 **(a)** 440 **(b)** 600 **(c)** 317 **(d)** 280

2 **(a)** 72 **(b)** 60

83. Problem-solving practice

1 Ruth

2

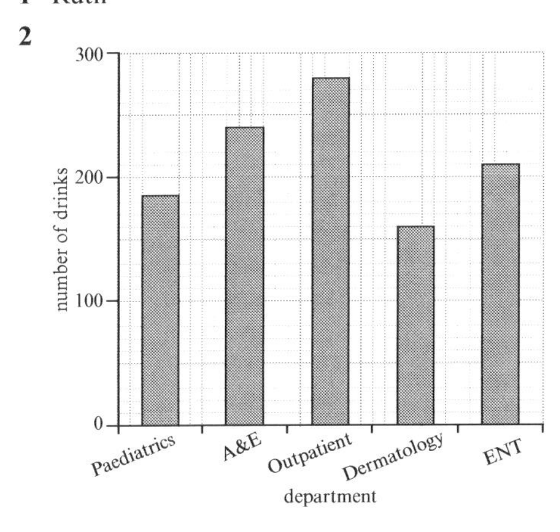

84. Practice paper

1 **(a)** 15% of £45 = $\frac{15}{100}$ × 45 = £6.75
No, she is incorrect.

(b) 2500 ÷ 20 + 25 = 150 minutes

(c) shop 1 = 4.75 + 3 × £2.85 = £13.30
shop 2 = £4.50 + 2 × £3.45 = £11.40
Emily should buy from shop 2

2 50 + 45 + 10 + 15 + 30 + 15 = 165 mins = 2 hours 45 mins
15:50 + 2 hours 45 mins = 18:35
No, she will not have enough time.

3 2 km = 2000 m

2000 ÷ 250 = 8

8 × 22 = 176
Tom is incorrect.

4 ABC = 35 000 + 25 000 + 42 000 = £102,000
GoGo = 29 000 + 39 000 + 27 000 = £95,000
She is incorrect.

5 **(a)** time = 150 ÷ 60 = 2.5 hours = 2 hours and 30 mins
7.15 p.m. + 2 hours and 30 mins = 9.45 p.m.
Yes she will.

(b) Tue/Wed/Thu/Mon/Tue/Wed/Thu = 7 × £30 = £210
Fri/Sat/Sun = 3 × £63 = £189
cost = £210 + £189 = £399

6

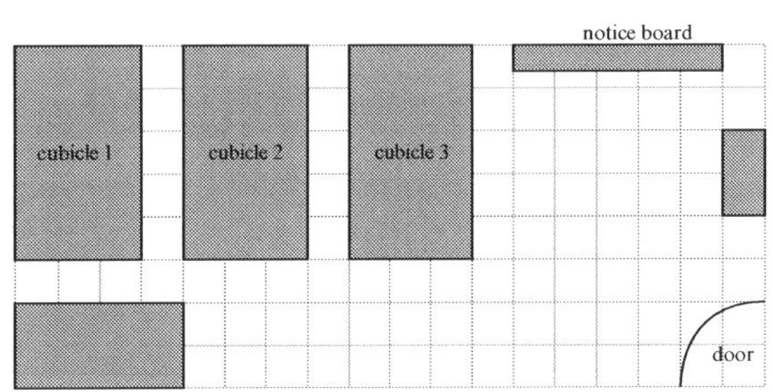

7 **(a)** 57.60 + 64.80 + 36.00 + 93.60 = £252
12 × £7.20 = £86.40
earnings = £252 + £86.40 = £338.40
He will meet his target.
check: £338.40 − £252 = £86.40

(b) mean = £1962 ÷ 6 = £327

8

Name	Petrol	Diesel	Small	Executive	Lease	Hire purchase
A						
B						
C						
D						
E						
F						
G						

9 **(a)** large = 4 × 15 = 60
small = 4 × 9 = 36
He should use 4 of each.

(b) £340 + £3 × 8 = £364
£364 ÷ 8 = £45.50
He is not correct.

Notes

Notes

Published by Pearson Education Limited, 80 Strand, London, WC2R 0RL.

www.pearsonschoolsandfecolleges.co.uk

Copies of official specifications for all Edexcel qualifications may be found on the website: www.edexcel.com

Edited, typeset and produced by Elektra Media Ltd

Illustrated by Elektra Media
Cover illustration by Miriam Sturdee

First published 2016

19 18 17 16
10 9 8 7 6 5 4 3 2 1

British Library Cataloguing in Publication Data
A catalogue record for this book is available from the British Library

ISBN 978 1 292 14562 4

Printed in Italy by Lego S.p.A.